Predators at Risk

IN THE PACIFIC NORTHWEST

Predators at Risk
IN THE PACIFIC NORTHWEST

DAN A. NELSON

THE
MOUNTAINEERS
BOOKS

Published by
The Mountaineers Books
1001 SW Klickitat Way, Suite 201
Seattle, WA 98134

First edition, 2000

Published simultaneously in Great Britain by Cordee, 3a DeMontfort Street, Leicester, England, LE1 7HD

Manufactured in the United States of America

Project Editor: Dottie Martin
Editor: Uma Kukathas
Cover and Book Designer: Kristy L. Welch
Layout Artist: Kristy L. Welch
Illustrator: Jim Hays

Cover photograph: *Alert mountain lion watches from pine tree.* © Howie Garber

Library of Congress Cataloging-in-Publication Data

Nelson, Dan A.
    Predators at risk in the Pacific Northwest / Dan A. Nelson—1st ed.
        p. cm.
    Includes bibliographical references (p.) and index.
    ISBN 0-89886-733-9 (pbk.)
        1. Carnivora—Northwest, Pacific. 2. Predation (Biology)—Northwest, Pacific.
        I. Title
    QL737.C2 N46 2000
    599.7'09795—dc21

                                                        00-009531
                                                        CIP

Contents

Acknowledgments

I owe a great debt of thanks to Margaret Foster and the rest of the editorial staff at The Mountaineers Books for their support of this book and of my writing. Through Margaret's support, I found a great partnership with The Mountaineers Books, and I appreciate the contributions of each and every person in the organization. I also owe a great deal to my colleagues at Washington Trails Association. Their support of my work outside the office has been outstanding and uncompromising, so thank you Elizabeth, Greg, Craig, Adam, and Chris.

Mitch Friedman, executive director of the Northwest Ecosystem Alliance, also has my hearty thanks for all his support throughout the years. I also owe much to the various men and women of the U.S. Fish and Wildlife Service and the Washington Department of Fish and Wildlife who have spent countless hours with me on the phone and in the field. These folks have dedicated their lives to wildlife, yet are often criticized from all sides. I appreciate their unflagging dedication to the wildlife of our state, and I salute their efforts even on the odd occasion when I disagree with their means.

My greatest thanks, though, goes to my family. As the youngest of five children, I grew up with a fantastic support system of my parents, sister, and brothers. Each of my siblings means a great deal to me, but in regards to my writing and passion for all things wild, my brother Jim has earned my greatest thanks. While I was struggling through my early teens, Jim—five years my senior—took it upon himself to introduce me to the outdoors through the time-honored tradition of hunting and fishing. I spent many afternoons in the field with Jim, hunting pheasants, grouse, chukar, and ducks. We caught many fish together (though, to be fair, he caught more—and bigger—fish than me), and through those many hours in the outdoors with my brother, I came to appreciate not only the wild, natural world but also the joy of sharing those adventures afield with another of like mind.

Jim also introduced me to backpacking, leading me into the Wenaha-Tucannon Wilderness Area while I was still an adolescent in high school. That experience set me on a path that veered slightly from the one he was to follow, but we both found careers in wilderness occupations. I drifted away from hunting, though I still have a passion for fly fishing, and turned to a world of trails and words as an outdoor writer. Jim, however, followed his strong dual affinity for the law and for wildlife and became a game warden, working for the Washington State Department of Fish and Wildlife. While our time in the field together has shrunk with each passing year, I still look back at our days together in the Blue Mountains and the valleys above the Snake River as some of the most enjoyable times in my life outdoors.

As much as Jim taught me about the outdoors, though, my parents taught me much more about life and the pursuit of happiness. My mother and father, Diana and Jim Nelson, are the most important people in my personal life and have had the greatest influence on my professional life. Not only did these two wonderful people bring me to the West when I was a mere toddler, introducing me to my beloved Western Mountains, but they also encouraged me to pursue my dreams, even when my dreams were to become a low-paid writer and photographer. The love and support I have received from my parents can neither be described nor overstated. Everything I am I owe to my parents, whom I love dearly.

Finally, this work could not have been completed without the incredible support I have received from Donna Meshke, my partner in all I do and all I am. Donna took care of our home—and of me—as I worked on this book and provided unquestioning love and understanding even as I neglected her and our life together while struggling through the long hours of creating this work. For that, and for everything else, Donna has my undying love and admiration.

Preface

My appreciation for wild things came early. My Midwestern family relocated to the West when I was just four years old, and it didn't take long for me to fall in love with the mountains around our new home.

Soon after arriving in Washington, my family took to the low, pine-covered mountains that flanked our small town. Growing up, my summers were filled with weekends in the Blue Mountains. We drove the old logging roads and hiked through thick pine forests. We hunted wild mushrooms and gathered juicy huckleberries. Wildlife was commonly seen on these outings, and soon I was able to tell the difference between a whitetail and a mule deer at a glance, and grew to love the big elk that roamed the Blues. But predators were largely unknown to me: We just didn't see many of the hunters, except for the occasional coyote trotting through the wheat fields of the foothills.

That changed one August day, and ever since I've had a fascination with, and deep appreciation for, predators.

I was just twelve years old. Three or four families were spending the day together on Maloney Mountain, picking berries and generally just enjoying the cool forests on the hot summer day. By mid-morning, the three pickup loads of parents and kids had ascended a network of old logging roads to find a meadow rich in ripe berries. We spread out with our buckets and began to pick. As I moved from one patch to another, I lost sight of my parents and the others in our group. But I knew where the trucks were, and I could hear the others talking just across the hill. So I continued picking, unconcerned that I was alone.

Following the ripe clumps of berries, I moved gradually up a gentle, berry-rich slope. I picked and walked, following the thickest clumps of berries without paying much attention to where I was going. Eventually I crested a small rise and was startled by a rustling noise in front of me. I went from startled to scared stupid in a matter of milliseconds as a black bear suddenly loomed up on its hind legs directly in front of me. I dropped my bucket of berries and turned with a shout and started away from the bear. By the time I reached the cluster of pickup trucks at the base of hill, I was breathless but safe—though the bruin could have been on top of me in a bound or two. Lucky for me, the bear had turned and rushed off in the opposite direction.

Later, I learned that every move I had made that day was wrong. I was a youngster alone in bear country. Worse, I was in prime bear feeding

habitat—a berry patch. I was moving silently, and when I encountered the bear I turned on my heels and ran like a scared deer. Fortunately, my bear was a youngster, too (once I calmed down and reviewed the encounter in my mind, I remembered the bear being not much taller than myself) and had apparently been as startled as I was. Today, when I look back, I can see that the bear had probably just been pushed out on its own that summer by its mother. Because it had to hunt up its own food for the first time in its life, it was probably too fixated on the food at hand (sweet berries) to worry about one puny little human "cub."

I don't know what that little bear thought of me, but from that day on, I was fascinated with big animals with big teeth and claws. I devoured the "gory and glory" stories about bear attacks and the unlikely survival of the unfortunate hunters/hikers/campers who were mauled and left for dead. I watched for any sign of cougars, bears, and coyotes every time I ventured out into the woods or high deserts of my childhood home. I felt a thrill every time I was fortunate enough to see a bear—which in my case was not that infrequently; by the time I was eighteen, I had seen no fewer than ten adult black bears and six cubs of various ages. I joined my brother in calling coyotes (he, armed with a rifle, me with a camera) and began to study the flights of raptors, eager to see their dive-bomb attacks on mice, snakes, and rabbits in the wheat fields around my home.

But my attraction to the predators wasn't just a fear-induced fascination with the natural hunters. As I studied the animals in the field and in the library, I learned to respect the skills of each species and to appreciate the beauty with which it moved and, yes, the way it killed. I learned early on that death is a part of life and that something often must die for others to live. I learned quickly that the natural world seldom if ever resembles the scenes shown on "nature" films. For instance, wolves aren't the creeping evil beasts that kill for pleasure as too many movies and books would have us believe. They don't circle the camps of wilderness travelers with evil intent. In fact, there is no record of healthy wolves ever attacking adult humans in North America. But that doesn't mean these animals fit the opposite stereotype, either. These are not gentle, benevolent animals that can be treated like the family dog. The wolf is a wild animal, and as such it cannot be defined by the standards of human behavior. No animal, wild or domestic, can be. The worst mistake humans make when trying to understand animals is to assign human

Facing page: Grizzly Bear (above), Black Bear (below)

responses to the beasts. Wolves, cougars, and bears may at times do things that make them seem human, but that's because we assign human motivations to their actions. This desire to anthropomorphize animals is a result of human nature—it's easier to project our own thoughts and ideas onto an animal to explain its actions than to figure out what's really going on with the critter.

I've spent better than twenty years pursuing my hobby of studying and trying to understand predators. I've read mountains of books, interviewed scores of biologists and wildlife professionals (as a journalist, I've been assigned many stories that let me continue my hobby of studying predators even as I worked), and sought out predators in the wild. But still I'm often amazed by the things I see or hear about when it comes to predators.

But I'm even more amazed at the general public's almost total lack of understanding when it comes to wildlife issues, and more specifically, predator issues. For instance, in recent years, cougars have been painted as the ultimate villain in the American West. There have been a half-dozen "attacks" in Washington alone over the past decade, mostly on children, and several hundred encounters reported each year. These reports have led some to believe that cougars pose an enormous threat to the safety and well-being of our children. Yet more kids are hurt by their classmates each year than have been hurt by cougars in the entire history of Washington State. But in the interest of child safety, some people—including several state legislators— would have us eradicate the cougars, or at least hunt them to the point where their population is so suppressed that they are effectively eliminated.

On the other hand, wolves have been the subject of an enormously successful public relations campaign that redesigned their public image. Where once they were inaccurately categorized as evil monsters, as seen in "Little Red Riding Hood" and "The Three Little Pigs," wolves are now painted with a much gentler brush. They are no longer the fierce, murderous beasts of our fairy tales, but gentle, caring, harmless animals of the teddy bear kind. Wolves are being welcomed back to wild areas they roamed long ago before being killed off, while cougars are being driven out of areas they've always inhabited. Likewise, black bears are welcome to stay in their wild lands, but grizzly bears aren't allowed to return to their former haunts.

The problem isn't that the different species behave so differently from each other, it's that people perceive them differently. Any predator—or wild

Facing page: Lynx (above), Bobcat (below)

animal of any kind, for that matter—is a potential threat to a human if the animal feels a threat to itself, its offspring, or the little corner of the world in which it lives. The animals keep to themselves whenever possible, but because they are wild predators who stay alive by the grace of their skill at killing, they are better able to defend themselves, their young, and their territory than are other species.

Humans need to understand that the predators are behaving naturally in a world that is increasingly altered and made less natural—by humans. Even the wildernesses and wild lands have been sculpted by our hands. The animals will learn, in time, to live with our alterations, even with our increasing presence into prime habitat. But we must learn also to live with their presence in the areas where we enjoy recreating. We have to do what it takes to minimize our impact on predators: Backpackers must hang their food from bear wires, or store it in bear-proof containers; parents need to learn to keep their kids at their side when day hiking on a forest trail—and to accept the fact that, at times, people and predators will have a conflict. The alternative is to eliminate all predators, and to most wilderness enthusiasts, that's not an option.

It is my hope that this book will offer some background and insight into the predator controversies and let you better understand the different species that grace our wonderful Pacific Northwest wild lands.

Chapter 1

Cougars: The Ghost Cats

I know what it is to be prey. I understand in some small way what it feels like to be stalked by something wild and ferocious, something with the potential to kill and devour you. I came to this understanding simply enough; I went for a hike.

In the autumn of 1999, while I was researching sections of the Pacific Crest Trail for a book, I found myself in the Panther Creek Experimental Forest of Washington's South Cascades. This region is filled with open forests. Sun filters through the broken canopy creating a mosaic of light on the green-and-brown forest floor. Grasses, graceful flowers, and thin, scraggly bushes grow in the dry hills and valleys beneath the towering firs, hemlocks, and pines. Few people hike this section of the PCT; it's far from the teeming population centers of the Puget Sound, and, even with Portland just a modest drive away, Panther Creek Forest lacks the majesty that draw hordes of hikers. There are no towering mountains, no cold alpine lakes, no thundering waterfalls, no meadows filled with wildflower blooms. There is just the trail and forest, with occasional views of the adjacent rolling hills.

So hikers, for the most part, ignore this commonplace locale. I, however, love this type of trail. I can walk for hours, losing myself in the quiet solitude of the forest, enjoying the companionship of jays, hares, and maybe the occasional deer. During this particular outing, I was alone on the trail, with not even another set of human tracks in the fine dust covering the path. Striding quietly but quickly up the trail, I noticed the wildlife around me. Birds flittered from branch to branch, a brace of Stellar's jays scolded a trio of squirrels, and the squirrels—unwilling to be lectured by mere birds—sassed them right back.

I noticed puffs of dust and a faint thumping on the trail ahead, and as I moved onward, I discovered their source. Tracks of a large hare were firmly imprinted into the dirt of the previously track-free trail. I scanned the forest floor around me, looking for the leg-eared bunny, but saw nothing: Either the hare had dived into a burrow or it was standing stock-still until I gave up and moved. Knowing I'd never see it unless it moved, I quickly gave up the search. Leaving the hare to scamper away in peace, I moved up the trail.

I continued to savor this relaxing walk through the woods all morning, finally stopping for lunch at midday. After a brief meal and a longer doze in the sunlight—filtered through the russet leaves of a stand of alder—I started back down the five miles of trail. I followed my footsteps less than a hundred yards when I found myself gawking at a second set of tracks. Lying directly on top of my prints were the huge tracks of a cat. I froze, staring at the prints. I knew the dry, powdery dust of the trail couldn't hold prints in pristine condition long—the loose dirt soon begins to crumble at the edges, and the breeze swirls more dust in to further obscure them. But these prints looked like they'd been pressed into quick-set concrete. There were no crumbling edges, no loose dust in the pad prints. These prints were fresh—so fresh that I could see the fine lines created by the fur growing between the cat's pads.

I was being followed. Instantly my breathe caught and my heart stopped. Then, with a faint whistle, I let my breathe out and my heart began to pound thunderously in my chest. Any thought of sleep disappeared in a flash as adrenaline rushed into my system. My conscious mind told me that cougars don't attack humans as a rule, and when they occasionally break that rule, it's not to attack a 200-pound man with a large backpack. Cougars are just curious, I rationalized. This cat was just watching to see what I was and what I was doing here. But even as my mind reasoned it all out, my deepest instincts were screaming, "To hell with reason, you're a puny human in the woods with a cat that kills 500-pound elk for breakfast." I knew I probably had nothing to fear, but knowing that and believing it are two different things—especially when you're staring at the track of a cat who's stalking you.

Pulling my eyes away from the tracks, I scanned the forest around me. The trees were widely spaced, and the open forest floor was devoid of cover for anything bigger than a rabbit. But I saw no cat. I looked back at the tracks and followed them with my eyes. I saw where the lion had obviously left the trail and climbed the gentle knoll above my lunch spot. I had been asleep there a mere ten minutes earlier—apparently under the watchful eye of a cougar. I scanned the forest one more time, looking for that tawny gold color common to all cougars (their Latin name, *Pumas concolor*, literally means "cats all of one color"). I saw no cat, not even a patch of tan.

By now, my desire to see the cat was beating out both rational thought and fear. Still, as much as I wanted to see the cat—I'd only seen one wild cougar in all my years exploring the wilderness—the prospect of stumbling around the forest in search of the beast didn't readily appeal to me. I knew cougars don't attack adult humans capriciously, but if I surprised it, or if I looked like a wounded buffoon ripe for the killing (and I have been known to stumble over my own feet, to say nothing of forest debris) it might decide to introduce me to its claws. Moreover, my rational mind told me that as soon as the cougar realized I knew of its presence—which would be as soon as I stepped off the trail and began to follow its tracks—it would disappear for good.

With no other real option, I turned and started back down the trail toward home. I focused on the tracks that lay on top of my own early tracks, although I also spent a good deal of time casting glances over my shoulder and staring at any bit of movement in the forest around me. I got one good jolt when a gray-and-tan grouse darted out from under a huckleberry bush near the trail, but didn't see or hear another creature stir the rest of the day.

For nearly 2 miles I followed the dual set of tracks. All along the way the cat's prints were neatly set on top of mine. When I came to the point where the cougar first dropped onto the trail, I spent a few minutes casting about for tracks in the brush above the trail. Finally, I found some tracks in a bit of soft duff above the trail, and so decided that the cougar had most likely been perched on a small rocky bench directly over the trail when I passed below him. Ever the curious beast, he had slipped in behind me to figure out what manner of animal I might be. This thought brought the chicken flesh to my limbs once more: I had been methodically stalked for more than 2 miles.

Or maybe not.

The fright-induced rush of adrenaline clouded my thinking momentarily, but after a few moments my pulse slowed and my thinking cleared once more. I was never in any real danger. If the cougar had perceived me as prey, I would have been brought down in the first couple hundred yards. No, I was followed not because I looked like a tasty morsel but simply because the mountain lion was curious about this two-legged beast wandering through his domain.

Curiosity Can Kill the Cat

Cougars possess a strong, innate curiosity. Captive cougars catch small bugs and rodents and study them for hours before either abandoning them or eating them. In the wild, an experience like mine is not uncommon. Cougars follow and spy on backpackers just to see what those bizarre, two-legged beasts are up to. Yet, attacks on healthy adult humans are virtually unheard of, even though cougars are used to catching and eating animals much larger than themselves. It could be that cats haven't learned to prey on humans— they are brought up killing and eating deer primarily, so they are accustomed to hunting four-legged beasts. But, it's also likely that humans don't behave like prey so cougars don't treat them like prey—a fact that should be lodged firmly in the minds of all hikers in case they do encounter cats.

Cougars are perhaps the most adept killers on the North American continent. They are solitary hunters who feed primarily on animals that are bigger than themselves. It takes a lot of skill, confidence, and intelligence for a predator to bring down an elk weighing four or five times what it does itself. But that's what cougars routinely do. The average weight for females is between 80 and 100 pounds, males average 120 to 180 pounds, and the biggest cougar on record is about 250 pounds, but elk can go 500 to 1,000 pounds. The cat has the benefit of tooth and claw, but the elk has size, strength, and deadly hooves to fight back with. But the mountain lion often prevails. Why? Because of its skill and intelligence. The cat knows where to strike the deer or elk to minimize its ability to fight back, and it knows better than to attack those individual animals that do put up a fight. Cougars eat only when their prey behaves like prey. That is, when the deer and elk they hunt are too frightened to defend themselves and instead attempt to flee. That's an important lesson for humans—fight, and the cougar will almost always back down. Flee, and the cougar will certainly attack.

It may seem odd that a predator as skilled and deadly as a mountain lion would back down from a fight with a clawless deer. But the cats know they live on a narrow line of survival. Studies performed by the Hornocker Institute, a leading researcher of big cats around the world that is located in Moscow, Idaho, show that up to 30 percent of cougar deaths occur while trying to capture prey. That is, a third of all cougars die as a direct result of their attempting to get food.

One strong kick to the ribs could crack or break one of the cat's ribs, putting it out of commission just long enough for it to starve. Further, a buck or bull who fights could hook the cat with a sharp antler, again killing or injuring the cat just enough to make it unable to hunt. Cougars lead dangerous lives. They have been found dead at the bottom of cliffs with their prey lying near them. The evidence here suggests the prey tumbled off a steep trail or cliff edge after being pounced on by the hungry cat. Cougar skulls have been found skewered on tree branches, apparent casualties of a leap gone bad, and crushed against rocks when a deer or elk managed to throw the cat off its back. The cats instinctively understand this and are genetically programmed to minimize their danger by backing down from prey that fights back. After all, the next deer in the herd will likely behave more normally and simply run away, thus presenting the lion with the chance to leap on its back and bring it down with a lethal bite to the throat.

The cougar knows the dangers of being a predator, and will minimize the risks when it can. But the cat hasn't yet learned that its greatest danger is often its own innate curiosity. The cougar that followed me walked away knowing a little more about humans, and I left the "encounter" with a strong sense of awe and wonder. Yet if the cougar had followed someone less familiar with predators, or with a greater fear of cougars, it could have ended very differently. I didn't report the incident to the state wildlife officials, but if I had the cat may have been tracked and killed, especially if there were prior complaints in the area, or if I had had small children with me at the time.

The vast majority of human "encounters" with cougars are similar to the scenario that played out with me and the Panther Creek cat. The lion sees a human and follows it at a safe distance out of curiosity. Occasionally, though, the cat gets careless or the human acts in a way the cougar didn't expect, and the human knows the animal is following at the rear. Instead of understanding that cougars are merely curious, some people assume they are being stalked as prey. The cats are then classified as problem animals and are often tracked and killed by wildlife agents or state-sanctioned hunters.

Curiosity does indeed kill the cat. Ironically, very few cougars would be killed in this way if more of us satisfied our curiosity about cougars. By understanding them better we fear them less and can better learn to live with these wild cats.

Cougar, Puma, Mountain Lion: Cat of One Color Is Cat of Many Names

The cat family *(Felidae)* is generally divided into three groups: large, roaring cats (African lions, tigers, jaguars, and leopards); small cats (including, among others, most species of the North American lynx, bobcats, and cougars); and the cheetah (this speedster is literally in a class by itself). The cougar, *Puma concolor* (formerly *felis concolor*), is the largest of the small cats. Cougars are unable to roar, and instead issue a high-pitched call that is frequently compared with a woman's scream. This call is only produced during the mating season or in periods of high stress.

The Latin name translates to "cat all of one color" but the cougar could just as easily be called "cat of many names." So many different peoples lived in cougar habitat—at one time (before Europeans landed on the shores of the New World) the cougar claimed the largest range of any land mammal in the western hemisphere—that the *Puma concolor* acquired a host of common names from those varied populations of humans.

Generally known in the West as either cougar or mountain lion, east of the Mississippi the animal is commonly called a puma, panther, painter, or catamount. The origins of these names are varied and in some dispute. The species is unique to the western hemisphere, but because of the cats' physical resemblance to African lionesses, explorers as far back in history as Columbus referred to them as lions, which was subsequently Americanized to "mountain lion." The name "cougar" dates back to an eighteenth-century French naturalist's corruption of the native Brazilian name for the cat, *cuguacuarana*. "Puma" is derived from the Incan name for the beast. C.T. Barnes notes in his 1960 book, *The Cougar or Mountain Lion,* that the cat has at least eighteen native South American, twenty-five native North American, and forty English names. The cougar is also reported to be listed in most dictionaries under more names than any other mammal in the world.

Cougars are solitary animals, each roaming a home range of 25 to 400 square miles, depending on density of prey and proximity of other cougars. They only come together to breed for a short period—typically just three or four days at most—before returning to their solitude.

The pregnant female chooses a safe, concealed place to give birth, but doesn't construct an elaborate den. Instead, the mother and newborn kittens, or cubs, change den sites several times in the first few months after the birth. A typical litter size is two or three kittens, but first-time mothers often have just one. The kittens are born with dark spots and baby blue eyes. As the youngsters grow, the spots fade and their eyes darken to a deep amber brown.

The kittens can stay with their mother for up to two years but typically leave, or are forced to leave, when they are between twelve and eighteen months. The young males seldom weigh more than 100 pounds during the first year or two they are on their own, and they slowly fill out to their average weight of 150 pounds. They tend to be lean and long, with a body length of up to 9 feet from snout to tip of tail. Their tails can account for a third of their body length. Females are generally 30 to 40 percent smaller than males.

While captive mountain lions have been known to live more than twenty years, the life span of a wild cougar is a little more than ten years, largely because they lead exceedingly dangerous lives. Accidents account for many cougar fatalities. That is a direct result of their lifestyle—they prey on animals that can be as much as seven times their own size (elk, for instance).

One wrong move during an attack and a cougar can be dealt a lethal blow from a hoof or break a leg—which almost certainly will lead to starvation.

Males usually live a bit longer than females, possibly because females have the added pressure of having to provide for their young as well as themselves for much of their lives. Females typically breed by their second year and usually have a litter every second year.

Cougars are ferocious killers, but the reality is that they almost always attack for just one reason: to eat. They will certainly fight for their survival if they feel threatened and cornered, but more often than not they choose to run rather than fight. This is why hunters use hounds to catch cougars—once the cat knows it faces no chance of winning the fight with the human and dogs, it flees. When that occurs, it's far easier for a hunter to simply let the dogs carry on the tiring work of the chase. Then, after the cougar gets tired and takes refuge in a tree, the dogs' barking leads the hunter to the scene where he or she can shoot the treed cat at will, with little or no effort.

That being the case, humans don't have a great deal to fear from wild mountain lions. Unfortunately, you have to understand cougars to understand that, and most people don't understand cougars.

These solitary killers are perhaps the least understood of all North American animals. They are rarely mentioned in Native American lore whereas other, more social animals like wolves, ravens, and bears are common. Perhaps because they didn't exist in Europe, they did not become part of the common mythology and legends of American folk stories. Cougars are ghosts who glide silently and often unnoticed through the woods, valleys, deserts, and mountains of the Americas. We don't know the animals, so we cannot understand them. Therein lies the reason why they are so feared, more so even than bears, despite the fact that bears are far more common and troublesome. Even naturalists and wildlife champions have misrepresented the little-understood cats: Theodore Roosevelt, who helped secure protection for many wildlife species, called cougars "craven, cruel killers." But they are far from craven. In fact—if we want to use human terms they are quite the opposite. After all, it would seem to require great courage and self-confidence to attack, and defeat, an animal six or seven times your own size! Cougars are not cruel killers, either. They are efficient hunters who kill for the most basic and acceptable reason—to eat and thus survive.

After several centuries of sharing the North American continent with the pumas, we still don't understand them. That is beginning to change, however, as more and more researchers turn their attention to these elusive cats.

Until more of that research is made known to the general public, however, these cats will be mistakenly perceived as a threat.

Cougar Attacks: Facts and Fiction

The Washington Department of Fish and Wildlife (WDFW) estimates that there are no more than 3,000 and maybe as few as 2,500 mountain lions residing in Washington State—compared to something like 35,000 black bears—yet in the last few years, there has been near hysteria over the dangers posed by rampaging cougars.

There has been a great increase in the number of complaints from the public regarding cougars on their property or near their homes. The WDFW reports a surge in complaints about cougar encounters. Indeed, the department's records show that cougar reports/sightings jumped from 247 in 1995 (the first year the department kept records) to 927 in 1998. The vast majority of these calls come from the new suburbs—developments that didn't exist ten years ago. In other words, from homes built in former habitat of cougars. Yet that doesn't explain all the complaints. Cougars have been spotted in old residential neighborhoods of Auburn, Spokane, and elsewhere. These are places that were developed and settled decades ago, that haven't been home to wild animals (other than the occasional raccoon and possum) since the Korean War. Why, then are there wild cats roaming them now?

The answer to that isn't as clear-cut as some would have you believe. Cougar numbers statewide are rising slightly. That rising population is certainly one of the reasons there are more complaints about cougar encounters. But there is a great deal of debate about why the lion population is growing. A few hunters and their allies in the legislature argue that the voting public is to blame. In 1996, voters overwhelmingly approved Initiative 655, which made it illegal in the state to hunt or pursue cougars, black bears, bobcats, or lynx with the aid of a dog or dogs. Without dogs, hunters are far less likely to kill a cat. The dogs are used to find, then chase the lion until it tires and retreats up a tree. Then the hunters follow the baying of the hounds—or rather, making the most of modern technology, the signals from tracking devices homed in on radio beacons attached to the dogs' collars—to the base of the tree where they then can shoot the cat at their leisure. There is no doubt this is the most effective means of hunting cougars. However, few people other than the practitioners themselves would consider this activity very sporting. That is why I-655 passed so convincingly—not because the general public abhors hunting, but because they demand that hunters be fair and treat the state's wildlife with respect.

Hound-hunting doesn't give the impression of fair chase, so the general public voted to ban the use of hounds. But that hasn't really contributed to the population increase, because while the number of cougars killed by hunters decreased as a result of the hound ban, the number killed by wildlife agents increased, meaning almost the same number of cougars were killed each year after I-655 became law as before.

To find the real answer to the population growth, we have to go back more than thirty-five years. It was in the early 1960s that the state stopped paying to have cougars killed. The practice of paying bounties began during the Depression, when the state was in the business of trying to eradicate all predators from public lands. The wolf was gone by then, and the cougar was the primary natural predator that threatened livestock, so the government offered a bounty of $35 for each dead cougar. That bounty was paid into the 1960s, when it was finally rescinded. By that time, however, the cougar population was decimated. And even after the bounty was removed, cougars were still listed as a varmint species.

There are two kinds of animals that hunters pursue: game animals and varmints. Game animals are deemed to be valuable prey for hunters and strict seasons and bag limits are imposed by the wildlife managers. Varmints, though, are deemed to be worthless or worse—they are considered to be undesirable. Hunters can kill as many varmints as they please, any time they please. Until the late 1970s cougars were classified as varmints and were routinely shot on sight and hunted year round. Mothers with young cubs were shot and the cubs often killed by pursuing dogs. But when the mountain lions were promoted to game animals, the number killed by hunters declined. No longer could enthusiastic hound hunters go out and kill as many cats as they could find. They were restricted to killing just one cougar per year, although they were allowed to continue to "pursue" hunt the cats throughout the year (i.e., "chase and tree" but not kill).

This reclassification helped the cougar rebound from what had become an abnormally low population. Since the early 1980s, the population of mountain lions in Washington has nearly doubled, with an estimated 2,500 to 3,000 cats roaming Washington today. So reclassification of the cougar as game plus the natural cyclical pattern of predator and prey populations are the primary reasons the population is growing today. Because the predator population is tied closely to the prey population, wildlife managers estimate that, given the deer and elk populations of Washington, the cougar population will level off at around 4,000 animals if left unchecked. That is, there will never be many more than 4,000 cougars roaming the 68,000 square miles of Washington (where, by comparison, the human population exceeds 5 million).

Despite these facts, a small minority of legislators still argue that the 1996 initiative is to blame, and they want to repeal the voters' decision. For a time, that seemed unlikely to happen—more than a dozen pieces of legislation were introduced during the 1999 legislative session and none made it to a full House vote. The next year, however, the hound hunters continued their push, this time narrowing their lobbying efforts to focus on public safety issues. The lobbyists drafted legislation that would partially repeal I-655 by directing the WDFW to allow—and encourage—hound-hunting of cougars in certain situations. Children who had been threatened—or even just *seen*— by cougars were paraded through Olympia's marbled halls as examples of "survivors" of the out-of-control cougar population. The bill breezed through the legislature as our elected representatives refused to object to anything that even remotely could be seen as having to do with child safety.

The bill was signed into law by Washington State Governor Gary Locke in March 2000 and went into effect immediately. The new law torpedoed only parts of I-655, yet wildlife advocates howled in rage. Cougars could once more be legally hunted with hounds. The law allows the WDFW to authorize the use of hounds to hunt cougars that are deemed a public safety threat, though the department is first supposed to ensure that no other practical alternative exists. The effect of this law won't be known for some time. The WDFW plans to study the issue and develop a course of action for its implementation while still abiding by the unchanged portions of I-655. Because even under the mantle of I-655, the WDFW could use hounds themselves for the removal of problem cats, it is unlikely that a great deal more cougars will be killed—they'll just be killed by someone who really enjoys it rather than by someone who is just doing his or her job.

The most drastic change wrought by the passing of the legislation may be to the initiative process itself. To date, our elected officials have been reluctant to touch any initiative because these laws are passed directly by the people and are therefore seen as being of utmost importance to the voting public. Yet, while more than 60 percent of the public sent a clear message that they disapproved of the use of hounds in hunting, the legislators let the baying hounds of the antienvironmental lobby tree them and push them to repeal the people's law.

The one thing this new law will not do is curb human–cougar encounters in the urban fringe. Findings from the Hornocker Institute point out that hunting may actually accelerate the spread of cougars into the urban fringe. Human hunters like to kill the biggest, most impressive animals, and that means the old, dominant males. These are also the cats that tend to control large blocks of territory, killing or driving off any weaker males that wander in. Because they claim such large blocks of territory—sometimes up to 100 square miles—any one part of the territory is visited only rarely. So when these dominant males establish a territorial range that touches on human habitations, they may prowl through the urban fringe once every few months, and are rarely seen if they do come close to their human neighbors.

But when one of these dominant males is killed, younger males rush in to claim the now open range. These younger, less experienced males may share the range, or fight to control it. Regardless, the end result is more cougars moving in close to the urban fringe. And because there are now more cats in the area, the food source is put under stress, and the young cats have to find alternate means to feed themselves. Because most suburban homes come complete with dogs or cats (or both), the cougars wander in to snack on Fido and Fluffy.

But cougars aren't always to blame for pet losses. In fact, cougars don't necessarily have to be present for an incident to be reported as a "cougar encounter." Home owners report cougar sightings when they aren't really sure what they have seen. In fact, this type of "cougar encounter" is far more common than a true encounter. Wildlife agents responding to cougar sighting calls have discovered yellow Labrador retrievers, large yellow house cats, and possums to be the culprits. In one almost unbelievable case, several home owners reported a large, black cougar prowling their backyards. After patrolling the area day and night, the wildlife agents captured this "black panther" only to find it wasn't a cat—it was a river otter.

This is not to say that people aren't encountering cougars. In the 100-year history of Washington, there have been nine documented cases of cougar attacks on people. Eight of those have occurred in the last ten years. Interestingly, the only cougar-caused fatality was an attack on a thirteen-year-old girl in the Okanogan region in 1923. In fact, of the 563 complaints the WDFW received about cougars in 1997, not one was about an actual attack on humans—the complaints were either reports of cougars seen near homes or recreational areas. That is, these weren't encounters that prompted the reports, merely sightings.

In fact, of all the cougar complaints the WDFW received from 1995, 1996, and 1997—a total of 1,305 reported sightings or encounters—only one, in 1996, was a report of an actual attack on a human. This one was another case of a child being attacked after wandering away from the family at a campground in northeastern Washington.

No one has been killed by a cougar in seventy-seven years, yet several members of the state legislature have made a repeal of the publicly approved ban on the use of hounds a priority out of concern for "public safety." Meanwhile, a person dies on a Washington highway every few minutes. Where is the similar concern for safety?

There is no call to reduce speed limits, focus law enforcement on unsafe drivers, or adopt new licensing standards to make our highways safer. Therefore, the proponents of using hounds to hunt cougars can't really be worried primarily about public safety—there are just too many other, more serious threats to our safety than a thousand wild cats. No, the real issue is an emotional one. Fear. Cougars are aggressive predators that, if they choose, could kill and consume any human they encounter.

Few people want to die, but to most people, the thought that they could be killed and be eaten by a wild animal seems far worse than simply dying in a car wreck. That is why cougars strike such an emotional fear with us: not that we could die, but that we could be killed as mere prey, as a meal for some wild beast. No matter how unlikely this is, the fact that it could happen drives some folks to want to battle the cougars into total and irrevocable submission.

Interaction Between Species

There are no easy answers when it comes to public policies, and that's never more true than when we're talking about environmental and wildlife issues. But as emotional as the cougar debates can be, good science can help clear the waters on this muddy issue. Unfortunately, though, when it comes to cougars there is remarkably little scientific research available. What research there is has largely been done by the Hornocker Institute, which is now in the midst of ground-breaking research into the relationship between cougars and other predators, primarily wolves and bears. Preliminary indications show some remarkable findings. For instance, while hunting groups have expressed concerns over the policies of predator reintroduction and recovery throughout the West because they fear the new populations of predators would kill too many deer and elk—animals the human hunters prize for themselves—the Hornocker research shows that this has not been the case to date.

When wolves and grizzlies were exterminated in the West, cougars found themselves at the top of the food chain, but now that those two species are making recoveries in some areas, the rankings get muddled.

A cougar can kill an individual wolf, but because wolves are pack animals they hold an advantage over the solitary cougars. When wolves were returned to Yellowstone National Park and the wildernesses of central Idaho, they encountered cougars, often to the cougars' detriment. Researchers found that wolves would drive cougars away from the cat's kills, often leading to the cats dying of starvation when they lost too many kills to the wolves. The wolves also would on occasion kill cougars outright if the cats were too close to the wolf pack's den.

Cougars that weren't killed directly by wolves were often forced to leave their territory and head into the territory of other cougars, who would then battle the newcomers. Again, the end result is a reduction in the cougar population. So while there is an increase in predator species when wolves are returned to an ecosystem, there isn't really a great increase in the amount of predation on the resident prey population, because as one predator population increases, another decreases. There is a similar effect when cougars encounter growing grizzly bear populations. Grizzlies can and do kill cougars, and they frequently steal prey killed by the cougars.

Nature tends to achieve a balance in all things. There will never be any more predators than the local prey population can support, and predators will never "kill off" an entire prey population because to do so would mean the destruction of their own species. And when two or more predator species hunt the same prey, those predator populations will adjust—in most cases, with the reduction in population of one predator species—to make sure that their combined hunting pressure doesn't push the prey numbers below sustainable level.

That balance can be upset by human interference, but it can also be helped along by humans. The choice is ours to make.

Cougars are a part of Washington's landscape and contribute to its beauty and majesty, but if they are to remain wild and free, human residents of the state must learn to understand them. We can live in the country adjacent to the big cats' territory, but to do so means respecting and understanding how cougars think and react. They are predators who want an easy meal. They don't scavenge—they only eat what they kill—but they will kill small animals when the opportunity presents itself. That means folks in the suburbs should keep the pets in the house after dark, and not let their kids wander into the suburban woods alone. They should not feed their pets outside because this attracts raccoons, possums, and other critters that in turn attract the lions. Eliminate these small scavengers and opportunistic feeders and you eliminate the cougars. In other words, take away the prey and you take away the predator.

Occasionally, folks encounter cougars while out hiking, trail running, or exploring the wild lands. Yet attacks on healthy adult humans are virtually unheard of even though cougars are used to catching and eating animals much larger than themselves. Again, the cougars don't seem to associate humans as prey. Therefore, the best way to encourage a cougar to attack you is to act like a frightened deer—turn and run away. As soon as you start running, the cougar's entire being shifts into instinctive autopilot and engages in pursuit.

So don't run. That leaves you face to face with a potential killer. What do you do?

First, keep in mind that the cougar is curious about you, and, as you stare at each other, several things are probably running through its mind: What are you? Are you a threat? Do you taste good, and if so, how easy would it be to catch you?

The more you can do to keep the cougar guessing and confused, the more likely it is the cat will move off to find more conventional prey. Steve Pozzanghera, predator specialist with the WDFW, says the first thing to do is move slowly but confidently. Stand up (if you are not already doing so) and make yourself look big and intimidating—maybe raise your arms, spread your coat, etc. It never hurts to talk to the animal. And keep eye contact; never turn your back or look completely away from the cougar. If the cougar is still hanging around, feel free to yell and throw things, but only if you don't have to bend down to get them. Don't crouch down to grab rocks or sticks to throw. Pozzanghera notes that there has been at least one case where a cougar attacked a person who bent down to pick up a rock to throw.

The idea is convince that cougar that you are not easy prey but you are also not a threat unless provoked. But the best thing to do, Pozzanghera is quick to note, is to "keep things in perspective." Cougars live a dangerous life and they know there is easier prey to catch than some curious two-legged beast that won't back down. Chances are that by the time you see the big cat, it will already be streaking away.

In the unlikely event that a cougar does attack you, or (as is more likely) a child near you, the best defense is a strong offense. Fight back. Kick, gouge and bite if you have to. Unlike grizzly bears, cougars don't let go if you play dead. They start to feed. So fight. Again, cougars aren't stupid and they know there are deer around that won't gouge at their eyes and kick their stomachs when attacked.

If you are hiking with children, ALWAYS stay within sight of the kids and be aware of what they are doing at all times. Cougars may attack a child alone, but if an adult is lurking close by, the cat will almost always stay away. If you do see a cat near a child, pick up the youngster. Or if the child is too old and heavy to easily pick up and hold, have him or her stand behind you. DO NOT tell them to run away. Again, you should follow the previously stated recommendations.

If you decide that you want to carry a little extra protection with you just in case you do stumble across a cat with an attitude problem, Pozzanghera urges you to forget guns and even the pepper sprays that are available. Pepper sprays and mace are designed for extremely close encounters, and the idea is to avoid having a close encounter. The best thing to carry is a compressed-air horn, which is compact and loud and obnoxious enough to scare away any animal that seems threatening, even if they are 100 yards away. Also, they are safer in the event of an accidental discharge: A ringing in the ears is much preferred to pepper in the eyes should you mistakenly hold the canister backwards.

Chapter 2

Lynx and Bobcats:
Close Cousins Who Live Worlds Apart

When two sets of tracks converge in the woods, and only one set leads away, there is little doubt what happened.

While hiking on the Pacific Crest Trail near Government Meadows on a sunny November morning, I discovered the unmistakable tracks of a snowshoe hare in the 10 inches of fresh snow that blanketed the forest floor. The tracks are unique in that the hare's back feet swing out and in front of the front legs, so the back prints are actually found in front of the prints from the front feet. So what I saw in the snow around me was a set of prints with two deep, angular imprints placed a few inches in front of two smaller, circular prints. The snowshoe hare had ambled through forest, under the brush, and over the trail for quite a while. A few dozen yards up the trail, though, I noticed that the tracks suddenly lengthened. The space between the tracks grew, and the imprints deepened, until finally there was 4 or 5 feet of smooth snow between the heavily smeared imprints of the big "snowshoe" prints.

Then I noticed the reason. Coming out of the trees on my left was a set of more subtle tracks. I backed up a few paces and moved off the trail toward these tracks. It looked as though this animal had been moving slowly and stealthily through the forest for some time. The tracks stayed close to tree trunks, and flowed smoothly around obstacles. Following these new tracks toward the trail, and the tracks of the hare, I found a spot where the new tracks seemed to stop. Four perfect imprints in the snow showed where the cat had paused and—because the snow was streaked as if it has been swept by a brush, or by the long fur of a bobcat's belly—crouched down to wait.

I stood next to the small rectangle delineated by the four paw prints and studied the scene before me. Less than 5 yards ahead of me was the Pacific Crest Trail on which I had been hiking, and in the snow on the other side of the trail were the prints of the snowshoe hare. At this point, the prints were still closely placed—suggesting the hare was still unaware of its watcher. I closed my eyes and tried to imagine what happened.

The hare was out in the twilight hours just before dawn to gather in its morning meal. It was browsing through the brush nibbling the last bits of greenery that weren't buried by this first, heavy snowfall. Meanwhile, a bobcat was completing its night prowl of the forest, looking for one last chance at a meal before curling up in a sheltered lair to doze away the day. The cat appears to have sensed the hare from at least 50 yards away—perhaps it heard it crunching through the wet snow, perhaps it smelled its musk scent.

Regardless, it became aware of the hare and instantly shifted into stealth mode, creeping cautiously up on the unsuspecting hare.

When the cat reached the point where I now stood, it undoubtedly could see the hare, but it didn't attack immediately. This was a savvy hunter. There was no cover between the two animals, so if the bobcat attacked too quickly, the hare might have time to get away. So the cat paused and dropped down onto its belly in the snow. I have no idea how long the wait was—the story told by the tracks doesn't include that kind of detail (at least, not in a way that I, with my meager skills, could read) but at some point, the cat attacked. Perhaps it was just waiting until the hare turned its back, or until it was busy chewing on a twig. Whatever it was, something eventually prompted the cat to launch its attack.

From the deep imprints in the fur-brushed snow at my feet, the cat leaped further than I could reach in one long stride (based on later measurements of my longest stride, I'd guess the cat's leap from a crouched position was about 4 feet). In just two or three bounds it was on the PCT—again, about 5 yards from where it launched the attack—and the hare, finally realizing it was being hunted, kicked up its own powerful "thrusters" and began to bound away.

The chase was a mere 10 yards long, ending in a yard-wide crater in the snow where the two had merged, and the hare had been overpowered by the sharp teeth and claws of the cat. Aside from the kicked up snow, there was a bit of grayish-white fur caught in the nearby brush, a small blot of crimson in the snow, and a thin line of red dots in the single departing track. It seems the bobcat, having caught its breakfast, preferred to dine away from the openness of the trail corridor. I considered following the hunter's track into the woods, but thought better of it. Not that I feared a confrontation with the cat—bobcats know better than to tangle with humans, or with any beast that is six or eight times its size. No, I chose not to continue along the tracks because I already had read the story of the tracks, and I didn't want to disturb the cat, which by now was probably done eating and already curled up and napping.

For me, seeing the tracks of the bobcat and the hare was more enjoyable than seeing the cat itself would have been. The tracks presented me with a story that I could read and enjoy without disturbing the animal. In fact, it's unlikely that many of us will ever experience a bobcat or a lynx in any other way. The small cats of our northern woods are elusive beasts that prefer to hunt at night, or during the quiet twilight periods.

Lynx and Bobcats: A Comparison

Canada lynx and bobcats are closely related cats. Both are in the Lynx family (bobcats are *Lynx rufus* and Canada lynx are *Lynx canadensis*), and they share a similar body appearance. Both have tufted ears, a flaring ruff of fur around the face, and a bobbed tail. But the cats, for all their common physical and biological traits, are very different.

Your average lynx or bobcat is about twice the size of a domesticated tabby cat. The bobcats weigh an average of 15 pounds (females) to 22 pounds (males) while lynx run about 18 pounds (female) to 24 pounds (male). Both species average about 30 inches in body length and have short (4- to 5-inch) tails. But the lynx stands 3 or 4 inches taller than bobcats, on average, due to their longer legs. The lynx is a winter-specialist and the longer legs, extra large feet (which, at up to 4 inches in diameter, are twice the size of those of a bobcat), and thick paw fur give it an advantage in navigating deep snow. Those broad paws serve as natural snowshoes to keep the cat afloat on or near the surface of the snow.

Bobcats are fairly common in Washington State. They live in nearly every county in the state and occupy a broad range of ecosystem types, from old-growth forests of Western Washington to the desert county of the mid–Columbia River Basin. Bobcats are still legally hunted and trapped in Washington as varmints. That is, there is no set season during which to hunt them, and no limit on their kill. The bobcats' cousins, the lynx, are far more rare. Lynx once roamed most of Eastern Washington, from the Cascade Crest to the other side of the Idaho border. But the cats were trapped extensively during the entire first half of the twentieth century. By the 1960s, the number of lynx was somewhat suppressed by the trapping efforts, but there were still enough of them to be a viable, stable population. Then came the 1970s and the rapid, near-total demise of the lynx in Washington.

Ironically, the lynx eradication was a direct result of international efforts to protect big cats. An international agreement known as CITES (Convention on International Trade in Endangered Species) was approved by most nations in 1972. This agreement was designed to stop all trade in the rare cats with spotted pelts, namely cheetahs, ocelots, leopards, and snow leopards. But Madison Avenue needed pelts to turn into coats for the jet-setting fashion crowd, so to fill the coat-making market after CITES, trappers turned to cats that offered attractive (if not spotted) pelts of thick, lustrous fur. In other words, Canada lynx. Suddenly, after the 1972 international moratorium on spotted cat pelts, lynx pelts jumped in price. Trappers who used to just scrape by were offered more than $500 per lynx pelt. As a result, there was a "fur rush" not unlike the gold rushes of the nineteenth century. Trappers took to the hills and laid out long lines of traps through the lynx-inhabited states.

According to state wildlife records, two trappers in Washington's Kettle Range took seventy lynx in just two winters in the mid-1970s, effectively wiping out that small, isolated population. In Montana, more than 700 lynx were trapped and killed each winter in the early 1970s. By 1978, though, the number of lynx caught declined rapidly to zero. The reason? The lynx were no longer there. The population had been decimated simply to provide coats for wealthy fashion mavens.

In Washington's North Cascades, however, the lynx was dealt one phenomenally lucky hand. When pelt prices blasted up $500 apiece, the remote lynx habitat in the North Cascades, from the Cascade Crest east to the Loomis State Forest, was still mostly roadless. Access to these areas was extremely limited. So trappers had a hard time getting close enough to the lynx habitat to effectively set their traps. That, combined with the fact that there were still lynx in other regions (such as the soon-to-be-decimated population in the Kettle Range) helped protect the North Cascade lynx. Then, during the 1980s when prices briefly jumped to $500 or better for a lynx skin, the North Cascade lynx was protected, not by their remoteness, but by the fortuitous timing of a federally funded study of their population. As part of the study, several lynx in the area were fitted with radio collars, so the entire North Cascade lynx range was closed to trapping.

The result of these two unrelated circumstances is that the eastern slope of the North Cascades harbors the strongest, most viable natural population of lynx in the Lower 48. But it needs to be remembered that "strongest" is a relative term. The population is far from strong; it is just stronger than any of the other threatened populations left in the country. Washington's lynx population numbers just thirty or so, but the small number of lynx here seem to be good reproducers. Several on-the-ground surveys have turned up pregnant or nursing females among the population, which shows that there is a strong chance that the lynx can survive here with a little help.

The Lynx's Last Hope

Canada lynx once hunted in half of the Lower 48 states: Colorado, Connecticut, Idaho, Illinois, Indiana, Iowa, Maine, Massachusetts, Michigan, Minnesota, Montana, North Dakota, Nebraska, New Hampshire, Nevada,

New York, Oregon, Pennsylvania, South Dakota, Utah, Vermont, Washington, Wisconsin, and Wyoming. Today, there are small but apparently viable populations in only two—Montana and Washington—with new evidence suggesting there might be a tiny lynx population in the Oregon Cascades. Colorado has begun its own lynx recovery program by reintroducing fifty lynx, live-trapped in Canada, to remote sections of the Rocky Mountains.

The State of Washington first began keeping track of and managing lynx hunting in 1933 when the state Department of Game was created. The lynx and bobcat were then listed as fur-bearers that could only be "taken" by trapping. However, no records were kept of the extent of the annual "take" of lynx until 1961. Beginning that year, trappers were required to submit reports of their annual catch, and in 1978, the Department of Game required trappers to tag their lynx pelts.

After the new reporting requirements were implemented in the early 1960s, the department also implemented stricter regulations on trapping. A specific trapping season was set, running an average of two months per year until 1977. In 1978, as the department watched the lynx harvest decline (and hence judged that the population must be declining), the trapping season was reduced to one month per year. Finally, in 1990, lynx trapping was closed in Washington. But the ban came too late. In 1993, the state listed the Canadian lynx as a threatened species.

Every other state had also banned lynx trapping—with one notable exception. In Montana, fur hunters today continue to set traps for the imperiled population of lynx that still hangs on in the remote regions of the Rocky Mountains.

Hunting and trapping certainly are the leading reasons for the demise of the lynx throughout their historic range. But the basic characteristics of the lynx have made its disappearance much more rapid and partially explains why lynx were wiped out across their range while bobcats thrive in their traditional territories and have expanded into country they never before occupied.

The easy way to explain the difference in character between the two species is to say that lynx are specialists while bobcats are generalists. Bobcats hunt just about anything they can catch and show a willingness to live in virtually any ecosystem. Lynx, on the other hand, prey almost solely on snowshoe hares and prefer to live in mid- to late-successional forest near old-growth stands. Research done as part of a U.S. government study of lynx shows that up to 52 percent of a lynx's diet consists of snowshoe hare, with another 30 percent being squirrels. This means that if the snowshoe hare populations decline, so too does the number of lynx.

Snowshoe hare populations tend to be fairly stable. When the number of hares dips too low, they just start breeding—like rabbits. A female can have up to four litters a year, with upwards of fourteen young per litter. So a single female can produce more than fifty youngsters each year. That sounds like a lot, but we need to consider what those bunnies face.

In addition to lynx, there are other predators, including coyotes, cougars, bears, bobcats, eagles, falcons, hawks, merlins, and wolverines who are ready to snatch up a snowshoe hare as a quick meal.

It's that competition that poses the threat to the lynx. Unlike generalist hunters such as coyotes, bobcats, and bears, the lynx focuses almost all its hunting skills on this one species. In the winter, this works out fine, because the lynx is uniquely qualified to hunt the snowshoe hare. It is the one predator that can keep up with the hare in the deep snows that blanket its high-elevation home ranges. In fact, most of the other predators move to lower elevation hunting grounds when the snow flies, leaving the lynx alone in the high country to hunt the white snowshoe hares.

However, if humans also use that winter wonderland for their recreation, they can lead additional predators into the lynx's range, putting extra pressure on the cats during their hard winter months. Snowmobiles and plowed roads are especially threatening to lynx. Coyotes and cougars, which aren't well adapted to travel in deep snow, follow the solidly packed tracks created by snowmobilers, and sometimes even those of skiers and snowshoers, to get into high country that would otherwise be inaccessible to them.

I've noticed this tendency myself. While snowshoeing in Okanogan country of the North Cascades in the late 1990s, I followed an old jeep track up a ridge. The snow was light and deep; even with snowshoes I was sinking a good 12 inches into the light powder. I hiked all morning, getting several miles deep into a remote wooded area near the southern border of the Pasayten Wilderness Area. After lunch, I turned around and started back down my track. I hadn't gone more than a mile before I looked down an open slope that I had traversed and saw a coyote lopping along in my tracks. As soon as it saw me, it bounded off into the loose snow and ducked into a thick stand of lodgepole pine, but there was no doubt that the coyote was using my tracks to make its own travel easier.

As a youngster, I once saw a bobcat trotting up a snowmobile track in the Blue Mountains of southeastern Washington. The snow was deep and light, but our snowmobiles had created a nice, fairly compact track about 2 feet wide. The bobcat had emerged from the woods and sprinted all out along the track as it crossed a broad meadow. Once in the trees on the far side of the clearing, it leapt out of the track and raced off into the more compact snow in the sheltered forest.

So human recreation has the potential to impact lynx, because humans literally create the pathways for competitors to move in and exploit the lynx's food source.

The greater problem, however, is that even if these additional predators don't cause a reduction in the hare population, the lynx are shy and don't like competition. If confronted, they almost always give up a kill, even to a smaller bobcat. So the lynx face two types of competition for their food. The first is called exploitation, or direct, competition, where two species hunt the same prey population. The second is known as interference, or conflict, competition, where one species aggressively steals food from the other and sometimes even attacks and kills the other species.

Exploitation competition is fairly common with the lynx because so many other species prey on snowshoe hares. The lynx usually end up the loser in these competitions because they are specialized hunters of hare, while the competitors tend to be generalists.

For instance, if great horned owls and redtailed hawks find a healthy population of snowshoe hares, they can hunt that population so extensively that there are too few hares left for the resident lynx to hunt effectively. The owls and hawks, sensing the depleted prey base, move on to hunt wood rats, voles, grouse, and so on, but the lynx is left without its sole source of food.

Interference competition is potentially more devastating to lynx, especially given their current population status in the Northwest (i.e., nearly extinct). A lynx can be driven off its kill quite easily by virtually any other predator of equal or greater size, which means nearly all the predators sharing the woods with the lynx. Fortunately, research shows that not all predators will drive a lynx from its kill, even if given the chance. Cougars, for instance, are nearly as specialized in their hunting practices as lynx (instead of hares, cougars focus on deer, elk, and other large ungulates) and seldom resort to scavenging or stealing. They will, however, kill lynx that roam into their territory, or that come too near a cougar kill. Cougars also readily kill lynx cubs when given the opportunity. It is common among predators to kill the young of other predators, especially when doing so doesn't put them into danger.

More generalized hunters, though, won't hesitate to move in on a lynx kill. Bobcats, for instance, will attempt to take a kill from lynx whenever they sense the opportunity. As successful as bobcats are at taking the lynx's felled prey, however, the greatest threat in this regard is the coyote.

Coyotes are extremely versatile and adaptable beasts that will take a meal anywhere they can get it, even if they have to steal it. And because lynx almost always abandon a kill when challenged by another predator, coyotes steal from lynx whenever they can. But coyotes also are an exploitation competitor; they also hunt hares. And because coyotes are so adaptable to any situation, and because they have a very high reproduction rate compared to other predators, they can exploit a hare population to such an extent that there is literally nothing left for the lynx to hunt. Thanks to humans and their growing interest in winter recreation, coyotes often can continue to hunt in the lynx's backyard even through the snowiest winters. They merely wait until a snowmobiler packs down a trail into a remote area and then cruise along the track into the previously inaccessible hare lairs.

Coyotes, then, potentially represent a serious threat to the recovery of lynx population in areas where coyotes have established strong populations of their own.

There is a simple, if unexpected, answer to this problem, however: wolves.

Wolves are also specialized hunters that focus on large hoofed animals, because they need to bring in enough food to feed a pack. Individual wolves will also hunt just about anything when traveling alone, but generally wolves don't compete with lynx for snowshoe hares, and they don't seem to be inclined to try to steal from lynx. Again, wolf packs require food in quantity, and there is just not enough meat on a hare to fully satisfy one wolf, let alone a pack.

So wolves aren't a threat to lynx. That alone doesn't help the cats, because they still have to deal with coyotes. Or do they? When wolves were eradicated throughout much of the United States in the first half of the twentieth century, coyote populations swelled and they moved into areas they never before inhabited. But whenever the wolf populations returned, either by natural recovery or by human-assisted reintroduction, the coyotes began to disappear. The reason for this is that wolves hate coyotes and usually try to kill them on sight. They dig up coyote dens and kill coyote pups. They drive coyotes out of their range, and when they don't outright kill them, the wolves steal food from coyotes, and literally starve them to death.

So, the reintroduction of wolves into lynx habitat can actually be beneficial to the lynx. And an added benefit is that, because wolves have the protection of being an endangered species, any habitat they occupy is granted a higher level of protection. By having wolves as neighbors, the lynx's home gets protected, too.

The Life of a Lynx

Lynx require habitat for their existence: habitat for foraging, for denning, and for travel. The requirements for foraging habitat are not those of the lynx, but of the snowshoe hare, because the lynx hunts wherever the snowshoe hare lives. The hare thrives in mid-successional (twenty- to forty-year-old) forest, especially lodgepole and ponderosa pine forests, and so the lynx is most often found hunting in this type of ecosystem. When it comes time to make a den, the lynx searches out areas rich with log piles (deadfall, windfall, woody debris), rocks, shrub thickets, and root tangles. These are generally mature (150-year-old) forests dominated by Engelmann spruce, subalpine fir, and lodgepole pine. The dens are often found on the northern and northeastern slopes of mountains, where these types of conditions are most common. In these dens, lynx produce one litter a year, with an average litter size of two to three cubs.

Between their stays in foraging areas and denning sites, Lynx use forests (with few prey) that have trees at least 3 feet taller than the snow level as travel habitat. This provides them with access to alternate hunting areas, as well as access to different prey species—such as voles, martens, and small rodents—when they can't find hares. It also furnishes cover from predators or bad weather. Often the travel routes follow major ridges, saddles, or riparian areas.

Though there have been lynx sightings throughout the eastern front of the northern Cascades, the lynx seem to primarily occupy the country in the eastern section of the Pasayten Wilderness Area and the adjacent Loomis State Forest. While the Pasayten is protected from development through the stringent restrictions on development imposed by the Wilderness Act, the Loomis has been managed as state trust land, meaning that proceeds from timber sales on the land are used to fund schools in the state. In the late 1990s, the Northwest Ecosystem Alliance (NWEA) fought to protect the Loomis through a variety of ways. Finally the organization, backed by strong public sentiment, forced the state Department of Natural Resources (DNR) to preserve some 25,000 acres on the Loomis Forest. There was a catch, though: the price. The DNR demanded that NWEA and its supporters pay the state trust fund the equivalent of what it would have received had the state sold the timber. After two years of arguing and fighting over the exact dollar figure—a fight made all the more bitter when the DNR suddenly, and unexpectedly, raised the price just months before the deal was to be finalized—the NWEA handed over the $16.5 million to close the deal and secure the protection of the high-elevation lodgepole pine forests of the Loomis.

The Loomis wild lands are ideal for lynx, as it provides them with the complete range of habitat they need. The northern segments of the Loomis provides denning habitat, some foraging habitat, and ample travel habitat. The southern quadrants of the Loomis provide greater foraging habitat, as well as denning and travel habitat. The complete ecosystem of the Loomis connects with adjacent lynx habitat in the Okanogan National Forest, the Pasayten Wilderness, and the wild lands of Canada.

In Washington, this area is the last, best place for the lynx to make a recovery. We simply need to give them the chance. Before the population can recover, the lynx and its habitat must be protected.

What Does the Future Bring?

In 1991, the National Audubon Society and eleven other groups petitioned the U.S. Department of Fish and Wildlife Service (USFWS) to list the Canada lynx as an endangered species in Washington's North Cascades. More than a year later, USFWS said that the petition didn't provide "substantial information" that the species needed to be listed. The original petitioners, this time led by the NWEA (then known as the Greater Ecosystem Alliance), almost immediately sued the USFWS over this finding, who then agreed to a settlement requiring them to reconsider their decision not to list the lynx.

In July 1993, the USFWS published a notice that there was still not substantial information to warrant listing, but that there was enough information presented by the petitioners to warrant an in-depth study of and status review of lynx through its traditional range. Fearing that this was just another foot-dragging effort on the part of the government to try to delay listing the lynx, the petitioning groups again applied legal pressure. A second settlement reached in November 1993 required the USFWS to publish the results of the status review by November 14, 1994. In April of that year, before the status report was finalized, the USFWS received another petition, this time requesting that the USFWS provide the Canada lynx with an emergency listing as endangered in the southern Rocky Mountains, specifically in Colorado. The USFWS found that petition presented a credible case and agreed that such endangered listing was warranted, but that an emergency listing wasn't necessary.

Later that year, the report that the USFWS had been required to provide under the 1993 settlement was issued. It stated that the lynx didn't warrant protection under the Endangered Species Act. The petitioners were shocked and struggled to regroup. How could this have happened? The State of Washington had already listed the lynx as threatened under the state's endangered species laws, but the USFWS apparently saw things differently. In 1996, the Defenders of Wildlife took the lead and sued the federal government over the 1994 report findings. A year later, the courts ruled on the suit and issued an order that struck down the unwarranted ruling. The issue was remanded back to USFWS for further consideration. The court also ordered that the USFWS publish a report on the status of the lynx within sixty days.

On May 27, 1997, six years after the original petition seeking Endangered Species Act protection was filed, the USFWS issued a report stating that the "Canada lynx population in the contiguous U.S. was warranted for listing under the Endangered Species Act, but precluded by actions on other species of higher taxonomic status." In other words, the lynx deserved to be protected, but the government was too busy to deal with it. The finding did automatically elevate the lynx to "candidate species" status, which offered at least some meager level of protection.

Meanwhile, Defenders of Wildlife and the other organizations participating the lawsuits were unhappy with the latest attempt of the USFWS to dodge responsibility for the lynx. The organizations took the government to court once more in September, 1997, arguing that the USFWS had violated the Endangered Species Act with its "warranted-but-precluded" ruling. The court agreed there were legitimate concerns about the health and well-being of the lynx populations and set an expedited court schedule and hearing date on the suit.

By February 1998, the plaintiff organizations agreed to a settlement with the government that required the USFWS to announce by June 30, 1998, whether they had enough evidence to continue considering the lynx for protected status in the contiguous United States.

In July 1998, that decision was published—the Canada lynx was worth further full consideration for protection under the Endangered Species Act— and the agency agreed to make a final determination of listing by November 1999. The plaintiff organizations agreed to accept having the lynx listed as threatened instead of endangered—a subtle change that allows the government more leeway in setting rules and restrictions for recovery efforts. But as the deadline neared, the USFWS reported it would need until January 8, 2000.

As that deadline came and went, Diane Katzenberger, spokeswoman for the USFWS, said the latest delay was unavoidable, as biologists needed more time than was allowed to review a comprehensive USFWS-commissioned report on the lynx. This latest study was completed on September 10 and was followed by a two-week public period during which 375 comments were received and had to be evaluated.

But the plaintiffs weren't buying it. More than a dozen organizations joined together in yet another lawsuit against the government on behalf of the beleaguered lynx. The lawsuit was filed, but the agency finally issued its decision on the lynx before the suit could move forward. In March 2000, the USFWS listed the Canada lynx in the contiguous United States as threatened under the Endangered Species Act. The listing protects wild cats, yet includes a provision that allows for the continued lawful possession, export, and take (euphemism for "kill") of captive-bred lynx. The threat to the lynx, according to the USFWS statements, stems primarily from lack of guidance to conserve the species in current federal land management plans. That is, the USFWS laid the blame squarely at the feet of the Forest Service for not protecting lynx habitat when creating its "get the timber out" forest plans.

Four regional lynx habitat cores were identified—the Northeast (Maine, New Hampshire, Vermont, and New York), the Great Lakes (Minnesota, Wisconsin, and Michigan), the Southern Rockies (Colorado, southeastern Wyoming), and the Northern Rocky Mountains/Cascades (Washington, Idaho, Oregon, Montana, northwestern Wyoming and Utah). Yet even as the agency identified these habitat areas, the USFWS argued that three of the four habitats weren't really important and only the Northern Rockies/

Cascades region was worth addressing. In the USFWS-issued press release that announced the listing, the agency noted that "in the Northeast and Southern Rockies regions, the amount of lynx habitat is relatively limited and does not contribute substantially to the persistence [of lynx]," and ". . . the Great Lakes Region does not contribute substantially to the persistence of the contiguous U.S. lynx population." In other words, there aren't many cats there anymore, and it's too much trouble to protect the remaining habitat, so we'll write-off those areas as too far gone and concentrate on the Northwest.

This attitude from the leading federal wildlife protection agency riled the groups that fought so long and hard for the lynx. Led by the Defenders of Wildlife, the loose coalition of predator advocates once more turned to the courts for redress for the wrongs done to the Canada lynx. Just weeks after the USFWS finally succumbed to the relentless pressure to do the right thing and then listed the cat as a threatened species, the Defenders of Wildlife and its allies notified the USFWS of its intent to challenge in federal court the legal and scientific adequacy of the agency's final listing decision regarding the Canada lynx. Under federal law, the groups had to notify the agency of their intent to sue at least 60 days before actually filing the lawsuit.

Of course, these groups applauded the listing, but they also take great issue with the idea that only one corner of the country—and even there, only the public lands—should be managed as critical lynx habitat.

In truth, the fourteen co-signers of the "intent-to-sue" letter have three primary concerns with the USFWS ruling on the lynx. The first concern was the agency's conclusion that three-quarters of the officially recognized regions—and all nonfederal lands—are unnecessary for the lynx's recovery. They also expressed outrage that the agency failed to list the lynx as endangered throughout the contiguous United States despite multiple threats to its survival. The endangered status would have increased the odds that the lynx would survive but also would have upset more politicians, so the agency went with the easier-to-explain (and brush-aside) listing of the lynx as threatened in the four regions. Finally, the plaintiffs noted that the USFWS failed to designate critical habitat for the species, relying instead on the goodwill of the other federal agencies—Forest Service, National Park Service, Bureau of Land Management—to create lynx-friendly use plans for all the lands they manage in the broad habitat regions.

The Canada lynx finally received protection under the Endangered

Species Act, yet that protection exists only on paper for now and the foreseeable future. The USFWS doesn't seem anxious to push for habitat protection, and it will likely take years before it can be forced to do its job of protecting the lynx.

Meanwhile, nearly a decade after the initial requests for federal protection of the cats, recovery and protection efforts are moving forward in some states despite the foot-dragging of federal biologists.

The lynx is on the Colorado State Endangered Species List. The last verifiable lynx sighting in that state was 1973. That is, the last sighting before Colorado's own recovery efforts were launched. While the Feds spend money in court, defending their foot-dragging, the state has been spending their cash on recovery. The USFWS refused to do anything about the decimated lynx population, so Colorado paid to have forty-one lynx live-trapped in Canada and flown into the San Juan Mountains of southwestern Colorado in 1999.

Nearly a year after the initial release of the lynx, more than half are still alive, which is considered a great success for predator reintroduction programs. Of the cats that have died, five starved, three were shot (in each case the lynx was claimed to have been mistaken for a bobcat), two were run over, and five died of unknown causes. One of the lynx didn't seem to like its new home and was eventually found dead (killed crossing a highway) in Nebraska.

The surviving lynx, though, seem to be doing well, and biologists believe that there are at least a couple of breeding pairs. In light of the success, Colorado has launched the second phase of the program, a planned release of another fifty lynx.

In Washington, the State Department of Fish and Wildlife listed the lynx as threatened in 1993, and nonprofit organizations such as Defenders of Wildlife, Friends of the Loomis, and the Northwest Ecosystem Alliance are working to protect the habitat of the remaining population of lynx in the state. The cash settlement that took the Loomis Forest off the timber block was a huge step toward the future recovery of the lynx in Washington. But until lynx receive the full benefits of protection under the Federal Endangered Species Act, they will be threatened by incidental kills (such as being caught in bobcat traps), their habitat will be further decimated, and there will be no human-assisted recovery programs to ensure the long-term viability of the remaining population.

Chapter 3

Coyotes: Masters of Adaptation

One story stands out in my memory. I don't remember the exact words—they don't matter—but the story sticks with me.

Long before European settlers set foot in the Pacific Northwest, back during the earliest days of humans in these lands, the animals helped create the world as it exists today. Coyote was one of the most prominent and wisest of the animals.

One day, during his travels, Coyote heard whispers that the new people of his land were being killed by a great monster in the Columbia River. This monster hid in a deep pool at Wishram (above the present-day site of The Dalles), where the waters ran swiftly through rock-lined channels. The monster was said to lurk in its pool and to pull down the two-legged ones as they paddled their canoes through narrow channels. The people were afraid of the monster and soon began to avoid the river, although this meant they could not catch the salmon that fed their children. More people died as they went hungry because of their fear.

Coyote had been waiting for these two-legged people to come into his land. When he heard the stories of the monster, he was angry and wanted to do something to help the people, but did not know how to defeat a monster that lived in a deep pool in the river. So Coyote went to the mountains and asked his friend, Raven, how to help the people. Together, Coyote and Raven came up with a plan.

Coyote gathered up a bundle of dry wood, with some pitch-wood mixed in, so he could make a fire. He put five sharp bone knives into his bundle. Coyote then headed down to the river to meet the monster.

Coyote stood on the bank of the deep hole where the monster lived and taunted the beast. At first, the monster wouldn't eat Coyote because it knew Coyote was a trickster and was afraid. But Coyote continued to taunt and laugh at the monster, mocking it until the beast rose up in anger and swallowed Coyote.

Once inside the monster, Coyote lit his fire and found many people huddled there. All were cold, wet, and near death. Coyote threw more wood on his fire to warm the people, and then used the first knife to carve meat from the monster's heart. This he roasted and fed to the people, making them strong once more.

As the people ate, Coyote used his knife to cut at the cords that held the monster's heart in place. Soon Coyote's knife broke. But Raven had known that the monster's sinew would be tough and so he had made Coyote carry five knives. Coyote retrieved his second knife and continued cutting the cords. When it, too, broke, he took up his third knife, and then the fourth.

Finally, with this fifth knife, Coyote had the cords nearly cut through, and the heart was about ready to drop out, which would then kill the monster. The monster—feeling death looming—suddenly coughed and the people and Coyote were flung onto the riverbank.

Coyote gave names to the people he had saved and sent them in all directions to occupy the lands. To the north of the river he sent the Yakamas and the Klickitats. To the south he sent the Clackamas and Clatsops. The Nez Perce and Cayuse went east, preferring to live among the hills and raise ponies. They also thanked Coyote for his help, praising his intelligence and cleverness in defeating the monster.

Once all the people had been sent to their new homes, Coyote looked the monster in the eye and said, "You must not eat the people anymore. If you do not swear to let the people use the river and catch the salmon that feeds them, I will jump into your throat and cut your heart loose."

The monster promised to let the people pass, but feared that he would die without anything to eat. So Coyote said to him: "You may shake the canoes in the rapid water and eat any of the people who lack the skill to paddle through them. In this way, the people know there is danger, and only those who are careless will feed you."

The monster agreed, and that is why some people still disappear in the rapids at Wishram. So goes the story, although today the rapids are deep under the reservoir behind the Bonneville Dam.

I've heard variations of this story from a number of different tribes of Native Americans. The stories differ slightly from region to region, but every form of the story, and others like it, all share one important component: The coyote is seen as a wise, generally gracious, being.

What makes it memorable for me is the fact that Coyote uses his quick wit and intelligence to help the people of the world. The local tribes revere him for this. Today, however, the coyote is reviled for his intelligence and ability to adapt to new situations. The coyote of the twentieth century has been stamped as a vile, cowardly beast, and as such, has been hunted mercilessly for the past hundred years and more throughout the West.

But which of these is the true nature of the coyote? Neither, I think, although I think the former comes much closer to the truth than the latter.

I believe that the coyote is a species that has never been fully understood by humans, largely because it is so adaptable. The coyote does what is required to adapt to any situation it faces. It will change its diet, hunting style, and even mating practices when necessary. The coyote's most consistent feature is its ability to change and adapt.

The Nature of the Wily Coyote

Trickster. The Wise One. The Monster-fighter. Moon Dog. Ghost Dog. Little Wolf. Sheepeater. Vermin. *Canis lantrans* (Latin for "barking dog").

The coyote has been given these labels and more by the people who know the animal best.

I prefer the Native American labels—the first three being my favorites and, I believe, the most appropriate given the coyote's wily nature. Coyotes have been part of native mythology and oral legends since people first moved onto the continent. Coyotes are native to North America, and, although they do seem to closely resemble species in other parts of the world—most notably the golden jackal of Africa—they are native only to the western United States and far southern parts of western Canada. Therefore, while no one fully understands the coyote, the Native American tribes of the American West are the people who best know the crafty canine.

Coyotes—pronounced ki-yo-tees by some, ki-oats by others (particularly folks living in rural parts of the West)—are perhaps the most adaptable, versatile predator in North America. They have learned to outsmart hunters and trappers, to avoid poisoned bait, and to take advantage of any opportunity to expand their territory. Coyotes still reside in all their native range, but have also moved into the rainforests of Western Washington. They have spread north to Alaska and south to Panama. They live in the Appalachian and Adirondack Mountains. And, most impressively, they have found good hunting in the urban wildernesses of major cities. Coyotes roam the streets of Los Angeles, and in the late 1990s a pair of coyotes caused a stir in downtown Manhattan: Apparently they moved in to hunt the local population of stray dogs, cats, and rats (the small, four-legged variety, not the two-legged types in business suits that are even more abundant there).

In Washington State, coyotes are native to the drylands and deserts of the Columbia Basin and the pine forests and sage brush hills of the Umatilla, Colville, Okanogan, and Wenatchee National Forests. They seldom, if ever, venture over the Cascade Crest into the wet forests of Western Washington. Today, however, the Washington Department of Fish and Wildlife (WDFW) classifies every square inch of Washington State as "core habitat" for coyotes.

That is, while other predator species declined in population, or outright disappeared, this small canine pushed its range, expanding out into areas previously dominated by wolves, cougars, and bears. The coyote now thrives in every county, and in many cities, of Washington.

Trickster indeed.

Growing up, I saw many coyotes in the wheat fields and mountain valleys of Columbia County, Washington. I never thought much about them and never considered trying to understand them; they were shadows that loped along the ridges and hills. I knew they were some kind of wild dog that the local ranchers shot on sight, but it wasn't until I was a teen that I came to appreciate the beauty and intelligence of the animals.

I have seen scores of coyotes during my time outdoors, but three encounters stand out in my memory. The first marked the day I learned to respect the wily canine. I was sixteen years old and working for a rancher in the dry hills nestled between the Blue Mountains and the Snake River. I was driving a truck and hauling dry peas from the fields to the local elevators.

Dry peas are harvested with a combine just like those used for wheat. The same basic combine is used, with a few simple modifications and one major difference. When harvesting wheat, the combine's header—the part that cuts off the grain and feeds it back into the separator units—is positioned well off the ground. The idea is to cut the stalk of wheat just below the wheat head so the combine gets all the grain but has as little straw to process as possible. A harvested wheat field is covered with a thick cover of standing straw.

Pea vines don't stand up like wheat stalks. By the time the vines wither and dry up enough to harvest (the peas must be bone dry before harvesting or they will rot in the storage tanks at the elevators), the vines are lying on the ground. So the combine is run with its header literally in the dirt, scraping the vines and the peas into the header so they can be severed from their roots and fed back into the bowels of the combine.

The field ends up clean, with nothing left standing. That's important to remember in this story. Another important point is that with pea harvesting the vines and pods move from the header into a "beater" that thrashes whatever comes in from the header until the pods break open. The beaten mass of vines, pods, and peas then feeds back across a series of shaker trays. The heavier peas fall through into an auger that dumps them into a large bin, or hopper, on top of the combine. The waste—vines, pods, dirt clods, etc.—rolls off the shakers and is kicked out of the back of the combine.

So what you have is a machine that scrapes up everything more than a few millimeters off the ground, separates out the peas (and any pea-sized dirt clods or rocks), and dumps everything else out of the back of the machine. That in and of itself wouldn't attract much interest from the local wildlife. But, the fact that field mice love pea fields does draw the interest of predators, especially hawks and coyotes.

During the summer, as the vines are growing, the mice are wonderfully safe scampering through the fields. The tight net of vines protects them from attack from the air and slows down ground attacks enough that the mice can easily scamper to a safe hole. But then come the combines, and not only is the protective cover torn from their field, but many of the mice are themselves scooped up by the combines. Of course they proceed to get thumped by the beaters, shaken on the trays, and blown out of the back by the powerful fan. Surprisingly, many of the mice are expelled alive and largely unharmed—although they are usually stunned and disoriented for a few moments. That's when the predators sweep in.

My first week working the pea harvest, I was amazed at the number of redtailed hawks in the area above us. As the truck driver, my job was to be on hand so the combine driver could dump his load into my truck as soon as his hopper was full. My truck could hold three full combine hoppers of peas, and it sometimes took hours to fill my truck. So I started studying the hawks and as a result discovered the living, but disoriented, mice in the combine waste trail. The hawks would wait until the combine was a good 50 yards away, then swoop down, grab a mouse, and climb back into the sky to find a perch to eat in peace. It was like watching planes circling a busy airport, waiting their turn to land, load up, and take off again.

On the third day in the pea fields I saw the coyote. He came toward the end of the day—we worked the fields from sunup to sundown—in the evening twilight. I was sitting in the cab of my truck, reading a book, when I sensed movement out of the corner of my eye. I slowly and quietly lowered the book and looked off toward the edge of the field. There, about 25 yards away in a rough cheat-grass strip along a shallow ravine, stood a coyote. He was staring at the combine as it slowly churned through the vines about 100 yards away. The coyote glanced up whenever a hawk dipped out of the sky, then watched the bird land and lift off again with its kill. After about fifteen minutes, by which time the combine had turned and was heading away from us, the coyote slowly trotted into the field and explored the ground recently vacated by the combine. Suddenly it lunged, tossed its head in the air, and chewed enthusiastically, its jaws stretching through mighty yawning-motions. It glanced left and right, then trotted forward, toward the combine. In another 15 yards it lunged again, tossed its head, and chomped down another mouse. The combine was now turning and heading toward my truck, so I drove under, let the operator unload in my truck bed, and then—because the light was fading—we called it a day.

Bright and early the next day, we got our equipment cleaned and oiled, and then started into the harvest once more. After the combine operator took off to begin cutting, I pulled out my binoculars and scanned the ravine in which I had first spotted the coyote the night before. It took about an hour, but finally I saw him. He was about half a mile way, trotting straight toward me. He entered the ravine and followed it back to our field, then paused at the edge of the field to watch the combine. As soon as it turned and started to cut away from us, the coyote trotted out and started scooping up mice. He followed along behind the combine as it circled the field, staying 100 yards or so behind. The hawks continued to dive in for their share, and for the most part, the coyote ignored them. But if a hawk dropped too close to the coyote, the coyote would lunge and leap at the hawk as it took to the air.

I watched the coyote catch and eat no less than a dozen mice before it showed signs of being full. But that didn't stop him from hunting. He continued to catch the mice, but now instead of merely crunching them down as fast as possible, the coyote would grab a mouse, and, with a flick of his head, toss it high in the air and catch it on the way down. At times, the coyote, who never seemed to notice me in my truck, was less than 30 yards way from me. I could often see the mouse, with its legs akimbo and its tail waving madly, flipping through the air before dropping into the toothy mouth of the coyote.

By late morning, with the temperature climbing into the high 90s, the coyote gave up this recreational feeding and sauntered slowly off to the ravine. Whether he bedded down under a cool bank or went back to his den, I don't know, but he disappeared for the rest of the day. Until the cool evening hours. About an hour before we quit for the day, the coyote came out again to grab a couple more mice.

The next day, I was sure the coyote would be back, and of course, it was. But this time he had his mate with him. The male, whom I watched the day before, came out shortly after the combine started cutting, but looked over his shoulder after catching each mouse. Shortly, a smaller coyote slunk out of the ravine and trotted over to sniff a mouse dangling from the male's mouth. The male let his mate smell the rodent before he swallowed it himself. As he loped forward for his next catch, the female was at his side. Then both lunged forward. The female was quicker, though, getting the mouse first.

They "hunted" like this together for a couple hours—this time not letting the hawks near the field—before running back to the ravine to sleep through the midday heat. The hawks, circling on the cool breezes overhead, fed on any mouse dumb enough to be caught out in midday. But as evening drew near, the coyotes returned for dinner.

The field we were cutting covered a long, sloping hill, maybe 400 acres in total. The combine could only operate at about 2 miles per hour, so we were in this field for three or four days. Every day, the pattern was repeated. I would stay confined in my truck while the coyotes hunted behind the combine. Then they'd go off to sleep somewhere for the bulk of the day, only to return in the evening for another meal.

I don't believe the coyotes had ever hunted this way before, but learned to do so by watching the hawks. In fact, I would go so far as to suggest that the presence of that many hawks—six or eight—in one place may have lured the coyote over. Coyotes are curious animals, and they are quick to learn, so it's possible they came over just to see what could bring so many raptors together. Or it could be that the coyote had previous hunting success by following hawks to their hunting grounds. Regardless, the fact remains that the coyote pair quickly learned to make the most of the situation, and they gorged themselves on a bumper crop of mice that week.

The story doesn't end there. We finished up that field and moved down the road to the next. I didn't see the coyotes again that year. But the following year we returned to an adjacent field of much smaller size and began to cut. Though the number of mice was far fewer this year than last, perhaps because so many had been made into coyote chow, the hawks soon appeared and began their airborne assault on the combine-stunned rodents. For the first two days I watched closely for any sign of the coyotes. He showed up again on the third day, this time alone. He was there bright and early, and ran through the morning feeding as if no time had passed since the last time he had done it. But the male didn't return to feed after the afternoon siesta. Rather, the female trotted out of the ravine with a half-grown pup at her side. The two of them ate their fill, then trotted toward the sheltered ravine. I looked up the hill toward the head of the valley and saw the flash of a tail as the male darted down into the grass and brush to rejoin his family. It appeared that he had been standing watch while the other two fed.

I saw them again the next day, and then we were on to the next field. I never encountered those coyotes again, but I will always remember them for opening my eyes to the simple, if deadly, grace of a predator hunting.

I should note here that my boss, a cattle rancher as well as a farmer, had initially been inclined to shoot them when I told him of the coyotes that first year. But when I noted that the coyotes were doing a good job of getting rid of the grain-eating mice, he dropped the issue and no more was said.

Unfortunately, not all ranchers are so understanding of the important role predators like the coyote can play in protecting their crops from booming populations of rodents. Thousands of coyotes are killed every year to protect ranchers' livestock, to reduce animal predation on wildlife favored by human hunters (namely, deer, elk, and antelope), and to protect pets in urban areas populated by coyotes. Most, though, are killed simply because they have the bad luck to have been seen on or near a ranch.

The War on Coyotes

Every year, the U.S. government kills more than 80,000—some years, as many as 100,000—coyotes throughout the country, mostly in the western states. Add in the coyotes killed by individuals or organized groups or hunters, and the count jumps to more than 400,000 coyotes per year. Hunters shoot coyotes for sport, and because they consider them as dangerous vermin. In some parts of the country, hunting clubs organize coyote competitions, in which shooters earn prize money for bringing in the most coyote hides in a given period, usually a weekend. Or, if the event is held during the spring or summer, hunters collect just the tail. Hides are virtually worthless at that time of the year, because the coyote is shedding its thick, lush winter coat and looks somewhat mangy and disheveled. The tail is used just to prove the kill, then tossed away to rot, just like the rest of the coyote's body.

This kind of hunting is hard to understand by anyone except those who participate in it. But it's even harder for me to understand the coyote hunts financed by the federal government. Again, tax dollars are used to pay for upwards of 25 percent of all the coyote killing done in the United States. According to their own records, the Wildlife Services, formerly Animal Damage Control (ADC)—the agency that runs the killing programs—spends nearly three-quarters of its budget on livestock protection. In other words, killing animals that might prey on domestic animals. With wolves being virtually exterminated throughout the country, and cougars never being much of a threat to livestock, Wildlife Service trappers and hunters focus largely on coyotes. Of the 91,749 predators killed by Wildlife Service agents in 1997, some 82,243 were coyotes.

All told, with a budget of $37 million, Wildlife Service agents killed more than 1.4 million animals in 1997, including 518,00 blackbirds and 667,000 starlings, mostly on public lands in response to complaints from private, for-profit parties.

Before I go on about the killing of the coyotes, I must point out an interesting side note about those birds. Because Wildlife Service agents can't take action unless there is a complaint filed, and then only if the complaint notes that people, domestic animals, or property are at risk, some of the reasons given for killing those birds begin to make sense. Interestingly, if the complaints are true, at least some of those birds should be classified in the "major predator" category with bears, wolves, cougars, coyotes, and foxes. According to Wildlife Service records, blackbirds in Arizona were responsible for the deaths of 2,400 adult cattle between 1990 and 1992. By contrast, coyotes were blamed for just fourteen cattle deaths in Arizona in that period. Meanwhile, in Texas, starlings preyed on fifty calves and twenty adult cattle in 1990. Perhaps Alfred Hitchcock was on to something in that classic movie, *The Birds*! Or maybe ranchers are simply manipulating the Wildlife Service program to get rid of critters they see as pests without having to foot the bill themselves. That is, ranchers seem to be finding ways to get a government subsidy to support their private business. And not just to get rid of birds, but also the bigger predators. From its inception in the 1960s and through the 1970s the Wildlife Service killers—then working under their ADC name— shot, poisoned and trapped nearly all the wolves and grizzly bears in the Lower 48. And then, at the behest of the ranchers, they moved on to coyotes.

That's odd, though. At one time, when wolves still roamed the hills, ranchers actually appreciated coyotes on their range lands. The coyotes killed a lot of rodents that would otherwise infest their homes and barns. The coyotes also ate a lot of burrowing animals like prairie dogs, which ranchers didn't like, because they created potential hazards to their stock; a cow that steps into a deep hole and breaks a leg is as good as dead.

Many farmers who don't own livestock still appreciate the rodent control provided by coyotes, but ranchers have turned on the coyotes, whom they now view as Public Enemy Number One. The abrupt change in attitude occurred after the wolves were exterminated. With the bigger, more aggressive canine predator removed from the food chain, coyotes quickly slipped into that higher position in the pecking order. More and more coyotes learned to hunt in small packs—basically large family units—and to exploit the expanded food supply left behind when the wolves disappeared.

Coyotes have become much more aggressive toward domestic livestock than wolves ever did, particularly the tender, easy-to-catch sheep that graze in ever-growing numbers around the country. No longer are coyotes seen as beneficial to farm and ranch. They are now perceived of as evil, sheep-killing, puppy-eating monsters that aren't worth the lead bullets needed to kill them. Gunfire, in fact, is one of the least popular methods of killing the hated coyote.

Agents working for the Wildlife Service have had to develop some unique, non-sporting, and seemingly unethical methods of killing when it comes to coyotes. That's because the coyotes learned quickly to avoid humans, as well as things like meat soaked in cyanide (they were put off by the smell). So Wildlife Service agents routinely hunt coyotes from the air, either in fixed-wing planes or helicopters. They trap them in lethal leghold traps and snares, they poison or burn coyote pups and nursing females in dens, and they use poison-delivery devices known as M-44s. These devices are hidden in meat and left in areas visited by coyotes—often, the baited M-44s are tossed from aircraft to achieve a wide broadcast distribution of them. The M-44 explodes in an animal's face when bitten, delivering sodium cyanide powder into the mouth and nose. Unfortunately, these devices are often deployed near areas inhabited by humans, and many domestic dogs have been killed by the M-44s.

While the major coyote-killing states are all in the Rocky Mountain and Great Plains states, Washington does experience its share of killing. With more than 3,000 coyotes per year, Washington ranks just thirteenth in order of states with the most coyotes killed. (The number one coyote-killing state is Texas, with nearly 20,000 coyotes shot, poisoned, or dynamited in their dens each year.) According to Wildlife Service records, Washington State received $521,929 in 1992. That was matched with state funds of $590,217, for a total budget of more than $1.1 million. With that, Wildlife Service agents were able to kill, among other things, 3,179 coyotes. More than 1,000 of those were killed with M-44s, while 257 of them were mere pups poisoned or burned in their dens. The rest were killed from the air (461), by traps and snares (1,008), or by shooting from the ground (368). On top of the Wildlife Service kills, another 1,875 were killed by private individuals who trapped or shot the coyotes for their furs, or just for the sake of shooting something.

The Washington coyote population was blamed for more than $123,000 in losses to the state's livestock herd in 1992. For a family-run farm or ranch, that is a lot of money, and it is easy to understand why some rural families despise coyotes. Still, there seems to be a lack of common sense in the response to these losses.

An average of $100 to $150 of the Wildlife Service budget is spent for each coyote killed, so in 1992, more than $300,000 was spent in Washington State to kill coyotes that were allegedly responsible for $123,000 in losses. By doing away with the coyote-killing program, the federal government could have provided each rancher with a sum that was double the amount of their losses and still come out $50,000 ahead. If they simply paid market value for the lost animals, the government would have saved more than $175,000 of taxpayer money.

It's a sobering thought also that the 3,179 coyotes killed in 1992 doesn't include those killed by the state's private hunters. Still, Washington has a large coyote population; estimates I've seen range from 50,000 to 120,000. Even at the lowest estimate, 3,000 isn't really all that many in relation to the population base. The Wildlife Service agents could kill two, three, or even four times as many coyotes and the population wouldn't suffer greatly. Coyotes are genetically programmed to rebuild their population as fast as possible in times of stress, so as the hunt increases, so too does the population.

In fact, recent studies indicate that the hunting pressure could actually be responsible for *increasing* coyote populations. A normal breeding pair of coyotes will produce a litter of two or three pups every two years or so. However, if that pair feels threatened, or if other coyotes in the area, especially other coyotes from their family group, are killed, their litter size will increase to seven to ten pups. Repeated studied have proven this—when a coyote population, or even just a single small pack, is put under stress, coyote bitches breed more frequently, and they produce bigger litters. In other words, by killing two or three coyotes in a given area, you might prompt a population increase of five or six coyotes. There is simply no way humans can counter this without sending out squads of hunters, seven days a week, twenty-four hours a day.

The Life of a Coyote

While the coyotes' resemblance to *Canis lupus* has prompted some residents of the West to dub them "little wolves," coyotes are quite different than wolves, although they do share a few common traits.

Coyotes are typically about half the size of wolves. Coyotes are native to North America, having evolved here. They are in the family *Canidea,* which makes up the species dog. In other words, they are cousins to *Canis lupus, Canis familiaris* (domesticated dogs), and *Canis rufus* (the red wolf). Coyotes are *Canis latrans,* Latin for "barking dog," so named because of their characteristic barks, yips, and howls. Within the species of *C. latrans,* there are more than nineteen subspecies, depending on the biologists you talk to. Some "subspecies" are nothing more than geographically isolated groups that have adapted and changed slightly to fit their new environments. But because that is what coyotes as a species do—adapt and change as needed to new situations and ecosystems—I find it hard to accept that every variation means a new subspecies. I prefer to think of the species "coyote" as one large, diverse species, just like *Homo sapiens.* After all, haven't humans, too, changed in body size, appearance, and diet, to meet the conditions of different ecosystems?

That's a debate for the biologists and academics, though. Whether the coyote is classified as one species or nineteen subspecies doesn't really matter. The important thing to remember is that coyotes adapt readily, and completely, to their environment. Therefore, coyotes in the high Rocky Mountains and in the remote hardwood forests of Maine tend to be larger and more robust than the coyotes that roam the desert Southwest or the open farmlands of the grain belt states. They also act differently.

In mountain country, coyotes rely less on rodents and small mammals for food and more on the larger prey species once hunted by wolves: deer and elk. To hunt these big ungulates, the coyotes have learned to live in large extended family units, or packs, and hunt as a team rather than as individuals. In essence, coyotes have moved in to fill the niche left when humans exterminated wolf populations.

But in areas where small prey is more readily available, such as farm lands and desert county, coyotes subsist largely on the rodents and small mammals. This being the case, a pack is more a hindrance than a help; it's tough to catch enough mice in one place to feed six or eight hungry predators. Therefore, coyotes tend to live and hunt alone, or as mated pairs, in these areas. They also tend to be smaller and more agile, while their cousins who hunt deer and elk tend to be heavier and more wolf-like in appearance.

Coyotes weigh 20 to 40 pounds on average, but some big males can push 80 to 100 pounds. They generally stand about 16 to 20 inches tall at the shoulder, and have longer, more pointed noses than do wolves. Coyotes' coats feature a dense, soft underlayer with a thick, heavy outer coat. The fur tends to be gray, with reddish-brown highlights throughout.

I have talked to and interviewed dozens of wildlife biologists about wolves and coyotes. I've been up close and personal with both species in wildlife rehabilitation parks, and have seen countless coyotes in the field. Yet after studying and researching wolves and coyotes for years, I nearly fell victim to a misidentification a few years ago, resulting in my second most memorable encounter with a coyote. While hiking in the Goat Rocks Wilderness Area near Snowgrass Flats, I came upon a broad, sloping talus field. The jumble of rocks houses a vocal, and seemingly large, population of marmots, so I approached slowly, watching the fat rock chucks scrambling around the boulders. When I was at the edge of the talus slope, I noticed a gray flash upslope from me. A quick look revealed what I took to be a good-sized wolf stalking a careless marmot just inside the talus. Wolf? I looked closer and saw that it was indeed nearly the size of a mature wolf, with a deep barrel chest and well-muscled haunches. But the animal also had tall, pointy ears; a slender, pointed snout; and tapered cheeks and forehead. Wolves have rounder ears, blunter snouts, and their face plains are concave. So what I was seeing was an incredibly large coyote. In the seconds it took for me to come to this realization, the animal sensed me and dashed off into the cover of the trees behind it. Feeling bad that I had interrupted its hunt, I moved on. I knew the coyote was lurking just out of sight, waiting until I cleared the scene, so I wasn't too worried about the disruption I caused. I was, however, excited to have seen the wonderful specimen of a coyote. It was easily 100 pounds and stood at least 24 inches at the shoulders—by far the biggest coyote I had ever seen. That fact alone made this encounter stand out in my mind.

Coyotes mate in late winter, usually as a bonded mating pair, although single males will often compete with a female's mate to try to "win her away." A mating pair digs a den, or finds a suitable already-made denning hole such as a hollowed out stump or small cave, and gives birth to a litter of pups in the spring. The litter may range from one or two pups to as many as ten, with the number often related directly to the number of other coyotes in the area, the availability of food, and amount of hunting pressure put on the coyotes by other predators, including humans.

The pups are born blind and totally helpless. They stay in the den for two to three weeks. Their eyes open after fourteen to eighteen days and they begin to stumble out of the den for short periods shortly after that. They nurse for up to eight weeks, although during the last couple weeks of nursing they also eat solid food. The meat is usually that brought back to the den by the father, either as solid chunks or as food that he ate and then regurgitated.

As the pups grow into adolescence through the summer and fall, they remain with their parents, learning to hunt and feed themselves. If they have the opportunity to hunt larger prey, they may remain with the parents indefinitely as new members of a family pack. But if they are in an area where the primary diet is composed of rodents, small mammals, and birds, they will usually leave, or be driven away, after the first year or eighteen months.

In addition to eating rodents, rabbits, deer, and elk, coyotes feed on just about any living thing they can catch. They are truly generalists when it comes to diet. Coyotes scavenge when possible, eating leftovers from cougar kills. They hunt quail, pheasants, and grouse. They eat snakes, frogs, and even bugs. In some areas, farmers have lost large portions of their melon crop to coyotes, and in other places, where natural food may be scarce (such as in urban parks and suburban fringe areas), coyotes develop a taste for house cats and small dogs, not to mention any dog kibble and cat food left outside by careless pet owners.

Coyotes can patrol a vast range quickly, and establish territories which they scent-mark and protect from other coyotes. But they also roam far abroad at times, moving into new locales whenever they can. Coyotes can lope along at a respectable 4 or 5 miles per hour all day long, and when they need to, they can reach speeds in excess of 38 miles per hour.

It is their ability and natural propensity to roam that has allowed them to spread from their traditional range—from the eastern front of the Cascades and Sierra Nevadas east to the Mississippi River, and from southern Canada to northern Mexico—to their current range—coast to coast and from Alaska to Tierra del Fuego.

My other most memorable experience with coyotes illustrated to me their ability to move into new lands, as well as their ability to exploit any food source in those new areas.

In the early 1990s I set out along Coldwater Lake Trail in the blast zone north-northwest of Mount St. Helens. The landscape was still one of devastation; the only greenery was low bushes scattered like big green dots among the jumble of gray trees littering the hillsides. There was a bit of grass along the lake shore, and several small clumps of fireweed and other wildflowers scattered across the slopes.

Just over ten years before my visit to Coldwater Lake, this area had been altered by the most cataclysmic natural event in our country's history. Mount St. Helens had erupted and the lands to the immediate north of the peak had been seared by super-heated winds moving at 600 miles per hour. Every living thing and been scorched and knocked flat. Nothing was left standing. Trees were laid down in perfect rows pointing away from the mountain. Animals and plants were incinerated, or suffocated. Even the ground was altered, as a heavy layer of ash followed burning winds. Gray, powdery ash coated the ground, making walking difficult for big animals, and impossible for ground-hugging beasts—they were literally drowned in the deep ash. The eruption also threw up a massive mud dam in the middle of valley, creating a brand new lake where none had existed before.

In short, the land was changed beyond recognition, and, it seemed, made totally uninhabitable. But what seems true seldom is. The land wasn't uninhabitable. It just needed adaptable species to return and begin the process of reshaping the landscape.

In the years following the blast, seeds were carried by the wind back to the blast zone. While these germinated and grew, the loose ash that blanketed the area was blown away, or compacted by rains and heavy snow-packs. The growing plants further secured the soils, opening the door for animals to return. The wildflowers I saw were the successors to those first plant colonists.

By the time of my visit that late spring day, elk were back on the hillsides of the Coldwater Valley, presumably because of those wildflowers—the plants present rich grazing opportunities, and the elk had come to take advantage of them. Of course, if elk could survive, small mammals had to be here, too. I didn't see them, but surely there were mice, wood rats, and other tiny critters living in the jumble of dead wood around me.

All these plants and animals had adapted to the harsh realities of the blast zone—no shade from the scorching sun in the summer, no protection from the winds and rains of the winter—and I was sure the most adaptable of all predators would be here, too, to take advantage of the opportunities presented by these new populations of mice and voles. They might, I thought, even try to hunt the elk.

Sure enough, about 3 miles up the trail, I came upon the coyotes. It was pure luck that I saw them at all. The trail was paralleling the northern side of the lake, and I had been watching a herd of elk on the southern side, directly opposite me. Between glances up at the elk, I watched the rough and rocky trail at my feet. While crossing a small ravine something caught my eye off to my left. The elk were to my right, and I hadn't been looking up the slope on the left for some time. But now I stopped and slowly scanned the hillside above me. I saw nothing, but I was sure something had moved, so I stood stock-still and continued to scan the slope with my eyes.

A few moments later, he moved. A large, gray coyote, almost the same color as the ash-gray slope behind him, trotted out of the shallow ravine and then darted into a tangle of brush about 50 yards above me. I pulled the binoculars from my pack and watched the bushes where I now knew the coyote was lurking. The plants covered an area about 5 yards in diameter, and I knew the coyote could be lying in there all day, waiting for me to move. Still, I thought I'd give it some time to see if it would become accustomed to me and move off again. I was anxious to see it more clearly, as it looked like an exceptionally large fellow.

I slowly dropped my pack and had a seat on top of it, never taking my eyes off the bushes hiding my coyote. Because of that narrow focus, I missed the other two coyotes until they were rushing into the bush, too. These two were smaller than the first, and I have no idea where they came from, except that they sprinted in from the same general direction as the first one.

After they entered the bush, things got interesting. There was some yipping, some barking, and some growling. Then the bushes shook like mad, and all was quiet for two or three long minutes. Suddenly, the first fellow trotted out of the bush with what appeared to be the leg of a large animal in its jaws. Half a dozen paces out of the bush, it stopped and looked down the slope at me, then trotted away up the slope on an angle, presenting me with a wonderful view of his side profile as he went. Through the binoculars, I could see that he was indeed carrying a leg—a plump, bloody leg of what had to be an elk. As the big male disappeared behind a swale on the slope, I swung my binoculars back toward the bushes to look for the other two.

I didn't have to look far. They were no more than 20 yards behind the first coyote, and each of them also had a good-sized slab of meat dangling from its jaws. From the size of these two, compared to the size of the first coyote, I guessed that they were the yearling pups. I stood, and with my binoculars in one hand and my hiking staff in the other, began to climb slowly up the slope toward the bushes. Not wanting to surprise any of them, as I climbed, I said in a loud, clear voice, "Hey, there, Mister Coyote. I don't want your meat, I'm just coming up to take a look. Don't mind me, Mister Coyote. Hey, ya!"

I reached the bushes and began to circle slowly around them. On the uphill side, I found the body. A small elk had caught a foreleg between two logs, breaking and pinning it under the larger of the logs. Perhaps from simple carelessness or because it was being chased, the elk had fallen victim to the landscape, not a predator. But that didn't stop the coyotes from enjoying the bounty of elk meat. The carcass was picked almost clean, with one rear leg completely gone (the one I saw the coyote carrying) and the other stripped of meat. The internal organs had been ripped out and devoured. Only the head remained largely intact.

I stared at the remains for a short time, then left it to the circling flies as I began to think about what I had just witnessed. My best guess was that the coyotes had either been chasing the elk when it got caught or had heard it thrashing around after it got caught and had then come in to devour it. Further, I'd venture that the three coyotes I had seen were three-quarters of the adult population of a local "pack," although I think family would be a more appropriate term. Two of them were considerably smaller than and obviously subservient to the third. My suspicion is that there was a fourth member, but that she was tucked away in a den with pups. That would explain why the coyotes I saw were carrying food away rather than just eating it where it lay. There were taking the food back to the nursing mother and her pups.

I hate to anthropomorphize, but the scene I witnessed, and theory I developed, makes me think of the coyotes as colonists or homesteaders, much like the humans who moved westward into the North American continent 200 years ago. They went forth as a family into a wild, unsettled area. They found the land harsh and the living conditions hard, but they worked together as a family, as a team, and survived and flourished in their new home.

I've gone back to the Coldwater Lake Trail several times since, and on more than one occasion I've seen coyotes or coyote tracks. Each time, I feel a thrill and a rush of happiness knowing these "colonists" have found a way to live and grow in the harsh environment of the Mount St. Helens blast zone.

The Coyote's Future

Coyotes are like our European colonists in another way. Now that they have spread into every corner of the country, it is going to be hard, if not impossible, to move them out. Even with the massive efforts of Wildlife Service agents, the coyote population continues to grow. In fact, the only place where coyote numbers are in a significant decline is in the areas where other predators are returning, namely, Yellowstone and central Idaho.

Coyotes invaded Yellowstone shortly after the last wolf was killed there early in the twentieth century, and established a large, dynamic population. The Yellowstone coyotes formed large family-based packs and hunted the park's deer and elk much like the wolves once did. In the absence of wolves, the coyotes joined the elite predators like the grizzly bear and cougar at the top of the food chain.

But once wolves were reintroduced into these ecosystems, the coyotes lost their place. The wolves have done what human hunters never could do: reduce the coyote population. The reasons for this are fairly simple: Wolves won't tolerate coyotes in their home range. They kill them on sight and drive them away from kills, so coyotes starve in wolf country even if they don't get killed outright.

When it comes to controlling the coyote populations, it could be argued that human hunters do the same things as the wolves—kill coyotes on sight. But humans are nowhere near as effective at controlling coyotes as wolves are. The reason is actually quite simple. Human hunters typically spend only a few days a year out gunning for the coyotes—even the most dedicated Wildlife Services agent won't hunt more than one or two days per week. Wolves are out there twenty-four hours a day, seven days a week, fifty-two weeks a year. Whatever they do, wherever they are, wolves keep an eye out for competitors—like the coyote. If the wolves encounter potential competition like the coyote, they'll pursue, harass, and try to kill them. And because the wolves are out there so much more than any human hunter, they do a much better job of controlling coyote populations.

If coyotes really do present the serious threat that some ranchers and landowners would have us believe, perhaps it's time for them to enlist some new hunters to replace the inefficient, and extremely expensive, Wildlife Service agents. Once upon a time, ranchers welcomed coyotes and despised wolves. Now that they despise coyotes, they would do well to welcome back the wolves. After all, they can control the coyote populations better, and more cost-effectively, than any two-legged hunter.

But even if that were to happen, and wolves would return to all their former haunts, the coyote will still thrive, though perhaps not so openly as it does now. No matter what changes come, the coyote will adapt and make the most of what it is presented with.

The Trickster will always stay one step ahead of the rest of us.

Chapter 4

American Black Bears:
The Country's Most Common Bruins

Geographically, Washington is the smallest of the contiguous states west of the Mississippi, yet it has the largest population. Not of people—with luck, we'll leave that dubious honor to California—but of black bears. With an estimated 30,000 to 35,000 black bears, Washington has more bruins than such wilderness-rich states as Idaho, with 20,000 to 25,000, Montana, with 15,000 to 25,000, and Oregon, which has some 20,000 to 25,000 black bears. In fact, according to Gary Brown in *The Great Bear Almanac,* of all fifty states, only Alaska has more black bears than Washington. There are more than 100,000 bruins roaming that state, mostly in the coastal forests of the southern parts of the state.

Given that high number of black bears, coupled with Washington's small size and large human population (the second largest in the eleven western states), I find it remarkable that there hasn't been much discussion of a "bear problem" in Washington. More than that, I find it somewhat frightening. I have witnessed too many instances of people underreacting to bear sightings, quite a contrast to the typical overreactions to cougar sightings. The problem is one of perception. Maybe it is fostered by having grown up with teddy bears filling our childhoods, but many folks look at black bears and see them as cute, somewhat clumsy critters that are lovable and harmless. I have seen hikers walk tossing sandwiches and granola bars at bears in an attempt to draw them into camera range. I've seen folks stop their cars and roll down their windows to get a look at bears standing in the road. I have heard accounts of people walking up and posing in front of bears—sometimes even taking their children with them!—so that their spouse could snap a picture of them.

One notable case in Washington's Olympic National Park comes to mind. A young couple wanted to have the local chipmunks come closer to their tent so they could get pictures, so they laid down a line of M&M candies from a jumble of nearby logs to their tent entrance. They then ducked into the tent with camera at the ready. Soon, they heard something moving outside, snuffling up the candy. Expecting a cute little squirrel, they got a chocolate-happy black bear. Their yells scared the bear away, but things could have turned out differently.

Stupid. Eventually the odds of a bear attack catch up with us, and we see a report in the newspaper about some hiker getting mauled, or about bears wandering into a town and dining on garbage cans, pet food, and sometimes on the pets themselves.

I've encountered more than two dozen black bears during the thirty years I've lived in this state. My first introduction to bears was on that warm August day I describe in the introduction to this book. That encounter in the huckleberry patch between the twelve-year-old me and the young black bear remains my most vivid recollection of a bear encounter. But others have also left their mark on my memory.

Nothing gets the heart thumping like the realization that you're standing between a female bear and her young. Fortunately, when I found myself in this situation in the Central Cascades early one September, the youngsters in question were yearling cubs, and momma bear, who was undoubtedly ready to toss the juvenile bruins out on their own at any moment, wasn't too concerned about my presence.

My partner Donna and I were out for a short day hike along the Pacific Crest Trail north of Chinook Pass. I was researching the route for a guide book, and Donna was along to enjoy the scenery and to keep me company. We chose this section of trail because I knew the huckleberries should be ripe along the way, and I'm a glutton for berries!

We started up the trail early on a Saturday morning, hoping to stay ahead of the hordes of hikers that would surely arrive at the trailhead later that morning. Still, despite our early start, we shared the trailhead with half a dozen other folks out for a quiet mountain stroll. Two gung-ho hikers hit the trail at a near-trot before we got our packs on, but we were soon on the trail behind them. That first pair was moving fast, and we found ourselves hiking along without another person in sight. That's when we heard it. We weren't more than a mile and a half up the trail when we heard a crash in the brush below us. We were traversing a 30-degree slope that was covered in huckleberry brambles with just a few trees scattered about. The ruckus was coming from a trio of trees growing close together about 20 yards downslope from the trail. I was a step or two in front of Donna, and when I turned at the noise, I saw nothing. I muttered something about a pair of squirrels fighting over pinecones, but Donna saw something bigger than a squirrel.

"Maybe a raccoon," I said, antsy to keep moving so we could stay well ahead of the other hikers. Donna wasn't ready to buy that argument, though, and kept looking at the trees. That's when the first two hikers came running back down the trail.

"There's a bear up there!" they gasped as they screeched to a halt in front of me. About then, Donna picked out the form of a bear cub in the tree branches and called out, "There's one down here, too."

The fast-paced backpackers weren't as far ahead of us as we had supposed, and had in fact encountered a large black bear just around the corner from where we stood. Knowing that it was undoubtedly the mother of the youngster in the tree below and slightly behind us, I knew we should clear out of there as soon as possible. The problem was that I didn't want to flee the trail, leaving the bears as a hazard for other, unsuspecting hikers. As I thought about the situation, two more hikers—an elderly couple with a small dachshund on a leash—came up behind us, making us a group of six. That, I thought, presented odds that not even a mother black bear would readily challenge. So I told the other five to stick close behind me and started slowly up the trail toward where the big bear had been spotted. Not 20 yards up the trail I saw a black rump retreating from the trail, heading straight up the hill. I stopped and watched. The sow slowly climbed about 15 yards above the trail, then turned into a rich patch of huckleberries and began to eat. Right beside it, I saw, was another, smaller bear. The mother munched a few berries, then slowly ambled away, heading back toward the direction we had come, but angling uphill away from the trail. The cub, a big, strapping yearling, watched me and the group behind me for moment, then grabbed a mouthful of berries, too, before taking off after momma. Suddenly, we heard crashing below the trail once more, and watched as the first cub dropped out of its hiding spot in the tree and raced up the slope to rejoin its sibling and mother.

Managing Encounters

This encounter could have unfolded in several different ways, and we were lucky to have had it play out as it did. If the elderly couple with the small dog had been the first to round the corner and come face to face with the matronly bruin, the dog might have upset the bear and prompted it to act more aggressively. If the cubs had been that year's cubs instead of yearling cubs, the mother would have been more protective and those first two hikers would have been attacked when they turned and ran. But as easy as it is to speculate about what could have happened, my experience has been that, more often than not, bears are even less interested than you in getting into a tussle.

Those three bears were the fifth, sixth, and seventh Donna and I had seen that year. In July, Donna and I crossed paths with a solitary bear along the Carbon River Road in Mount Rainier National Park while on a biking and hiking outing. And in late August, we spotted a large male browsing through the berry patches on Mother Mountain near Spray Park on the northwestern side of Mount Rainier. And late in the spring, while visiting my folks at their home in the Blue Mountains of southeastern Washington, we sat on the deck and watched a couple of bears amble through their backyard, within feet of the house.

Seven bears in a single hiking season. A remarkable number considering the fact that in the previous twenty years I had seen roughly fifteen black bears in the wild, less than one per year on average.

I was thrilled to see so many wild predators, but also a bit concerned. This was not so much for myself as for my fellow backpackers—and for the bears. Because when bears and humans encounter each other, the bears are typically the losers in the end.

Bears are classified as omnivores, which technically means they eat both plants and animal matter. But in realistic terms, it means they are opportunistic feeders—they'll eat whatever is easy to get at, be it plant, animal, or Powerbar. Generally, vegetation makes up the bulk of a black bear's diet, because plants are the easiest, and most common, source of food in a bear's range. But when the opportunity presents itself, bears will eat small animals, bugs, and even large ungulates. And when dried turkey tetrazini and M&M-rich trail mix are available, they'll gorge themselves on these, too.

So what hikers need to do is keep their food out of reach of bears. Simple as that. Unfortunately, too many backpackers fail to take into account the bear's incredible resourcefulness. Still others fail to take into account the bears at all. I've seen hikers eating in their tents, dirty pots left lying in the middle of camp all night and food bags hung a mere foot or two off the ground (essentially at mouth level for a roving bear) right next to tents.

Unfortunately, bears stealing humans' food is not the end of it. The problem doesn't go away after a bear ransacks a poorly protected camp. Bears aren't dumb. Indeed, they are generally quick-witted, remarkably resourceful, and have long memories. Once a bear learns that hikers carry tasty treats, it begins to associate all our colorful packs and nylon stuff sacks with food. The bear will be watching future hikers in that area, looking for ways to get an easy meal from the portable pantries we call backpacks.

That's happening more and more often, it seems. Too many backpackers have been careless with their precautions, most notably in Olympic National Park. The popular Elwha River Valley Trail faces what appear to be annual closures due to the presence of boorish bears who have learned that hikers carry good food that is easy to get to. Every summer, all it takes is a few campers who fail to safely store their provisions. The bears find the food bags that have been left within reach and ransack their rucksacks and feast on their food.

In 1998, the Elwha Valley Trail was closed in May while a pack-ransacking bear prowled the area. A week or so later, he moved on and the trail was reopened. But then on July 3, hikers camped in the Marys Falls Camp in the lower Elwha Valley neglected to take the precaution of hanging their food safely out of reach of bruins. Another roving bear found the food bag and promptly gobbled it down. This incident prompted the park to re-close the 6.6-mile section of trail between Lillian Camp and Elkhorn Camp.

After rangers installed secure "bear wires" on which campers must hang their food bags, the Elwha Trail was reopened. Meanwhile the even more popular backcountry camps on the Seven Lakes Basin and the High Divide were closed down. Barb Maynes, spokesperson for Olympic National Park, said at the time that three separate bear–human encounters, again involving improperly stored food, prompted the park service to ban camping until further notice at Seven Lakes Basin, High Divide, Heart Lake, Cat Basin, the Potholes, and along the northern section of The Bailey Range.

The three Olympic National Park incidents involved bears plundering backpacks and campsites when the humans were out of the area, so no humans were directly threatened by the bruins. But the Park Service deemed the threat great enough to close the area to further hiking until the bears moved on to greener pastures. Similar problems have occurred throughout the state. In the North Cascades National Park Complex, during the same year that the closures in the Olympics took place, two backcountry camps, Rainbow Creek and Thunder Basin, were closed because of bears getting into backpacks and food storage bags.

Again, no human was directly threatened, but because the bears had gotten into humans' food, use of the camps was restricted until the bears left the area. Meanwhile, a Park Service volunteer staffing a lookout tower on Desolation Peak was afraid to leave her post because a black bear was lingering around the base of the lookout. Biologists were called in to monitor the bear's activity and make a judgement about its temperament and likely actions. The biologists, after a short observation, noted the abundance of huckleberries in the area and pronounced the bear's behavior as normal and appropriate to the area. The bear was left alone to finish its berry feast, and when the crop was fully harvested, the bear went looking for other food. In this instance, the land managers exercised remarkable restraint and good judgement—the bear wasn't punished simply because it wandered into an area used by a few humans. Rather, the humans were forced to adapt to the bear's presence.

Campers who hiked into the Desolation Camp area on the flank of Desolation Peak were required to carry bear-proof containers to eliminate any chance that the bear would find food and become a "problem bear" (i.e., one that associates humans with food).

The Desolation Camp bear encounter was a positive example of how we can live together with predators. The bears were left alone to act like bears, and the human visitors were trained in how to reduce their impact on the wild animals whose homes they were visiting.

Bears of all kind tend to prefer solitude to human company, and black bears generally flee long before you have a chance to get too close. There are times, however, when bears either don't hear people approaching or they are more interested in defending their food source—or their young—than they are in avoiding a confrontation. These instances are rare, and you can further minimize the odds of an encounter with an aggressive bear, by doing the following.

◆ Hike in a group and hike only during daylight hours.

◆ Talk or sing as you hike. If bears hear you coming, they will usually avoid you. On the other hand, bears feel threatened when surprised, and often go on the offensive in a surprise encounter, at least until they feel the threat is neutralized. So make noises that identify you as a human. Talk, sing, or rattle pebbles in a tin can, especially when hiking near a river or stream, which can mask more subtle sounds that might normally alert a bear to your presence.

◆ Be aware of the environment around you, and know how to identify "bear signs." Overturned rocks and torn-up deadwood logs often are the result of a bear searching for grubs. Berry bushes that are stripped of berries, with leaves, branches, and berries littering the ground under the bushes, show where a bear has fed. Bears often leave claw marks on trees, because they use trees as scratching posts, and fur in the rough bark of the trees is a sign that says "a bear was here!" Tracks and scat are the most common signs of bear's recent presence.

◆ Stay away from abundant food sources and dead animals. Black bears are opportunistic and will scavenge food. A bear that finds a dead deer will hang around until the meat is gone, and it will defend that food against any perceived threat.

◆ Keep dogs on their leashes and under control. Many bear encounters have resulted from unleashed dogs chasing a bear. The bear gets angry and turns on the dog, the dog gets scared and runs for help (i.e., back to its owner), and the bear follows it right to the dog owner.

◆ Leave perfume, hair spray, cologne, and scented soaps at home. Using scented sprays and body lotions makes you smell like a big, tasty treat.

Unfortunately, not all hikers behave as they should in bear country, especially in camp. Bears are intelligent animals, and, again, they are opportunistic feeders. That's why some bears have learned that sloppy hikers can provide good, tasty meals. They have learned to watch human camps and to look for the slobs among us. To avoid being seen as a "sloppy hiker," make sure you do the following.

◆ Never eat or cook in your tent. Spilled food or even food odors can permeate the nylon material, essentially making your tent smell, at least to a bear, like last night's dinner.

◆ Never clean fish within 100 feet of camp.

◆ Always store all your food and other scented items in their own stuff sacks when preparing to hang them. Don't use your sleeping bag's stuff sack for food, or the food can be transferred to the sack and then to the sleeping bag, making the bear think you are a big, smelly meatroll.

◆ Always suspend your food bags at least 12 feet in the air and 8 to 10 feet from the nearest tree trunk. In some popular backcountry camps, land managers provide wires, complete with pulleys, to help you do this. You should learn how to string your own rope to achieve these heights, too.

◆ Never try to lure wild animals closer to you with food. You may be trying to attract a cute little pica, but get instead a big scary bear.

On rare occasions, hikers can do all the right things and a bear will still behave aggressively. It could be as simple as being in the wrong place at the wrong time—as I clearly was when I encountered that sow with cubs. If those cubs had been first-year cubs, I would have been in a situation where the bear could have turned aggressive in an instant, despite the numbers of other hikers I had grouped behind me. The thing to remember is that bears are individuals and they don't conform to a standard set of rules of behavior any more than humans do. If you find yourself in a situation where the bear behaves aggressively or in a way you did not expect, here are some guidelines to follow.

- Respect a bear's need for personal space. If you see a bear in the distance, make a wide detour around it, or if that's not possible, that is, if the trail leads close to the bear, leave the area.
- If you encounter a bear at close range, remain calm. Do not run, as this may trigger a predator-prey reaction from the bear.
- Talk in a low, calm manner to the bear to help identify yourself as a human.
- Hold your arms out from your body, and if wearing a jacket hold open the front so you appear to be as big as possible.
- Don't stare directly at the bear. The bear may interpret this as a direct threat or challenge. Watch the animal without making direct eye-to-eye contact.
- Slowly move upwind of the bear if you can do so without crowding it. The bear's strongest sense is its sense of smell, and if it can sniff you and identify you as human, it may retreat.
- Know how to interpret bear behavior. A nervous bear will often rumble in its chest, clack its teeth, and "pop" its jaw. It may paw the ground and swing its head violently side to side. If the bear does this, watch it closely, without staring directly at it.
- Continue speaking calmly and in a low voice.
- Resist the urge to run. A bear may bluff-charge—run at you but stop well before reaching you—to try and intimidate you. Don't run from this charge, as that would turn the bluff into a real charge and you will NOT be able to outrun the bear. Black bears can run at speeds up to 35 miles per hour through log-strewn forests.
- If you surprise a bear and it does charge from close range, lie down and play dead. A surprised bear will leave you once the perceived threat is neutralized. However, if the bear wasn't attacking because it was surprised—if it charges from a long distance, or if it has had a chance to identify you and still attacks—you should fight back. A bear in this situation is behaving in a predatory manner and is looking at you as food. Kick, stab, and punch at the bear. If it knows you will fight back, it may leave you and search for easier prey.

◆ Carry a 12-ounce (or larger) can of pepper spray deterrent. Make sure you get one that is rated for use on bears, as the kind commonly sold as anti-mugging or personal self-defense sprays don't contain a strong enough pepper solution to deter bears. The spray, a high concentration of oils from hot peppers, should fire out at least 20 or 30 feet in a broad mist. Don't use the spray unless a bear is actually charging and is in range of the spray.

Growing Concern Over Bears

Even if everyone follows these guidelines and adopts "bear safe" practices, there will still be encounters between people and bruins. It's simply inevitable when we share the same environments. Of course, not everyone does adopt these practices, and that's one reason humans are encountering black bears more and more often. Seldom do people really understand what they are dealing with when it comes to bears. These creatures are not the non-violent cartoon characters that steal pick-a-nick baskets and pester grouchy forest rangers. They are potentially deadly beasts.

The Washington Department of Fish and Wildlife (WDFW) reports that complaints about black bears jumped from 208 in 1995 to 541 in 1997. As a result of those 541 complaints, 37 bears were captured and relocated, 16 were killed by WDFW agents, and 26 were killed by others. In none of the cases did a bear actually threaten a human—they killed pets, they roamed through yards, and they stole food, but they didn't attack anybody. That's not to say they won't, but the fact remains that bear attacks are still a statistically tiny threat.

That fact doesn't dissuade some avid bear hunters, though, from trying to overturn a law passed by the people of Washington in 1996. Initiative 655, which banned the use of hounds to hunt cougars and bears, also banned hunters from using bait while hunting bears. This was the most reprehensible act addressed by I-655. Even hunting groups have long opposed this practice as it involves no sportsmanship whatsoever.

The basic premise of "baiting" is to create and maintain a feeding station for bears right up until hunting season. So-called bear hunters find an area they deem to be good habitat for bears, then find a tree nearby where they build a stand—a platform about 12 to 20 feet off the ground on which they sit and watch the feeding station. They stock the feeding station with whatever bait they can find. Some hunters used stale old donuts from their local donut shop, others used refuse from butcher shops or grocery stores.

They restocked the station every couple days until the local bears became accustomed to coming there for a fast, easy meal. Maintain the feeding site long enough and the bears not only became accustomed but dependent on the handout.

On opening day of hunting season, the hunter brings out his rifle and climbs into his stand. From there, he can watch the bears line up for dinner. The hunter picks out the biggest of the bears that stops by, shoots him from the stand, and drags the bear home after the successful "hunt." Again, most self-respecting hunters would never stoop to this practice, and several hunting organizations actively endorsed the initiative that banned the practice. They did this not because they oppose hunting—and, indeed, I do not oppose hunting—but because the practice of bear-baiting casts a bad light on the entire hunting community.

That hasn't deterred practitioners of baiting to try to reverse the law, however. They have found champions among a few members of the state legislature and have been introducing legislation every year since the passage of I-655 to have it reversed. They argue that it's a matter of public safety, and that they only want to bait to stop the slaughter of our state's citizens by the hordes of savage bruins that threaten us.

To date, the efforts to reinstate baiting as a legal practice haven't gone far—every attempt has died in committees. But someday, the baiters might get a victory if people continue to misunderstand the nature of black bears.

The Life of a Black Bear

The American black bear is unique to North America, and is one of the most stable, secure species of bear in the world. Other bears, like our own grizzly (brown) bears, sun bears, and Asiatic black bears are threatened or endangered, but the American black bear population is as strong today as it was the day the Mayflower landed at Plymouth Rock. Biologists estimate there were about 500,000 American black bears in North America then, and perhaps as many as 650,000 today. Black bears once lived in 49 states (no wild bears have ever lived on the Hawaiian Islands), and they now live in forty-two. They are extinct in Delaware, Illinois, Indiana, Iowa, Kansas, Nebraska, and Ohio because their habitat has been destroyed, i.e. logged, or developed into farm land.

The name "black bear" was appended to this species by early European settlers, because the bears of the eastern seaboard states tended to be a lustrous black color. But the American black bear doesn't have to be black. These bears range in color from almost snowy white to deep, glossy black. The white-phase bears are found only in a small area of British Columbia and are known as the Kermode bear, or ghost bear. Most of the black bears in Washington are truly black, although I have seen several cinnamon-colored bears in the Blue Mountains of the southeast corner of the state. I've also seen some dark russet-colored black bears in the Central Cascades.

The American black bear averages 200 to 250 pounds for an adult male and 100 to 150 pounds for an adult female. These bears are solitary animals, coming together to mate, but then separating shortly after mating is over. The female raises her litter of cubs alone. The litter size typically runs from one to three cubs, although as many as five are possible. The baby bears are born in the mother's hibernation den in late winter, and are totally helpless at birth. Weighing an average of 12 ounces when delivered, they are born blind and nearly immobile. At 12 ounces, the cub is about 1/280th the weight of its mother, whereas a human infant is about 1/25th the weight of its mother at birth. But the youngsters grow quickly. Their eyes open after about a month, and they gain weight rapidly: At eight weeks, they average five pounds, and at six months, about 50 pounds. That fast growth is a testament to their mothers.

A lactating black bear sow produces milk that contains more than 33 percent fat and nearly 15 percent protein. Human milk contains just 3.5 percent fat. Because the first couple months of the cub's life are in the den, the sow is in essence passing on its own body fats and proteins to the nursing cub. A pregnant bear can lose nearly half of her body weight while hibernating and nursing the newborn. It's not surprising, then, that it comes out of the den in spring hungry and ill-tempered. This is perhaps the worst time to encounter a bear; it will most likely be hungry, cranky, and ready to take a bite out of just about anything.

The cubs, meanwhile, come out of the dens fat and happy and ready to explore. For the next several months, they follow their mother around the woods, learning what to eat, and how to find it. They stick with mom through the summer and join her in the hibernation den in late autumn to spend the winter with her, staying warm under the snowpack. They stick with her through the next summer, but they are generally chased off late in the summer, at 18 months or so, to fend for themselves. Sometimes siblings stay together through the next winter's hibernation period, but they invariably split up the following spring to pursue their own lives.

The bear's hibernation period varies from region to region, and generally, the further north a bear lives, the longer it will hibernate. Black bears take to their dens earlier than grizzly bears, and in Washington most black bears head for bed sometime in October or November, and remain there through April at least. At higher elevations, bears may stay in their dens until May. The big, mature males are always the last to den up and the first to emerge in the spring. Pregnant sows are often also among the last to den up—they need to eat as much and for as long as they can—but are also the last to emerge with their nursing cubs.

Black bears generally search out a suitable den long before they plan to use it, then spend the last few weeks of the autumn in the area near the den so they are close by when they decide to take their long winter's nap. They might seek out a cave to sleep in, but more commonly they scrape out a hole under a fallen log, crawl into a hollowed out stump, find a hole among a jumble of boulders at the base of a cliff, or simply dig a cavity under a thick, dense clump of brush. Bears have been found hibernating in plugged culverts, and in the crawl spaces of houses and cabins. The ideal location for hibernation is a sheltered, well-insulated space with a narrow opening. Bears sometimes dig 6 feet into a hillside to create that shelter.

In the northern latitudes, black bears may add 4 inches of fat to their bodies prior to hibernation, and they lose all that during the months of inactivity. To get the extra fat for the winter, they consume vast amounts of food—gaining up to three pounds per day at times.

Black bears live in nearly all natural environments, and are opportunistic eaters. They are omnivores, meaning they eat both plants and animals, but for the most part they stick to plants. Berries, roots and grasses comprise the majority of their diet, but they hunt small birds and animals at times, and will never pass up a good meal of carrion. That is, they will readily scavenge food, even if it means stealing a kill from a cougar or coyote.

Unfortunately, it is their opportunistic traits, and generalist approach to eating, that causes problems for hikers and rural homeowners. All it takes is a strong scent to attract the bear's attention. It could be the scent of cat food on the porch, or spilled spaghetti sauce in camp. The bear possesses a remarkable sense of smell, and has a nose with a direct line to its stomach.

I read a report on the Internet about a black bear attack on a group of Boy Scouts. The youngsters were hiking along the Appalachian Trail. After stopping and pitching camp, they cooked their dinner of fried hamburgers. They cleaned up camp after dinner and put away their food, but didn't bother to think about their clothing. So, they went to bed with the odor of hamburger grease in their T-shirts, in their hair, and on their skin. Later that night, a lumbering bruin happened by, smelled the wonderful odor of cold burger grease, and proceeded to tear through camp looking for the source.

One of the boys was mauled badly before the others were able to drive off the bear. The boy survived, but was scored by deep cuts and bites. I believe he later returned to the woods and became an advocate for cooking well outside of camp when in bear country (which is pretty much anywhere there are wilderness trails worth hiking), always washing up, and hanging scented clothing—even if it is merely scented with deodorant—with food bags.

Here I'd like to back up a bit. I said that early spring, when the bears are coming out of hibernation, may be the worst time to run into the bears. But the late summer and early autumn period is when the bears are most deadly.

When the nights start to get a little cold, the bears know their time is limited. They instinctively understand that they aren't going to get anything to eat all winter long—they have to live off whatever they can chow down on right now. So, they go into hyper-feasting mode. September is one of the busiest months for bears as they gorge themselves, trying to put on as much weight as they can for their long winter in the den. According to biologists at Northwest Trek Wild Animal Park in Pierce County, during the autumn feeding rush black bears gain an average of 2 to 4 pounds per day. They are actively scrounging for food twenty to twenty-four hours per day, and they will not pass up a meal of any kind. They suck down every berry they can find, dig up grubs and slugs, graze on rich grasses, and devour any animal they can catch. They also get more aggressive about snatching gorp-filled backpacks and ripping through messy campsites.

There are more than 30,000 black bears in Washington, and a growing number of hikers heading for the hills; in 1998 there were an estimated 1.6 million hikers in the state, according to a Sporting Goods Manufacturers Association survey. September is one of the finest months of the year to hike in the Cascades and it is also the month when black bears are most actively searching for food. This combination creates a perfect opportunity for problems.

Fortunately, humans can minimize the risks by simply being aware of the bears and understanding how and why they behave as they do. By taking the time to safely bag and hang all food and scented items—safely meaning at least 10 to 12 feet off the ground, and 10 to 12 feet from the nearest tree trunk—chances of an encounter are cut to next to nothing. If all cooking is done at least 100 feet from the tent, and all food and scents (like perfume, deodorant, soaps, etc.) kept out of the tent and off clothing and skin, the odds of an encounter drop even more.

So plan well and a bear sighting can be a thing to cherish and enjoy. Plan poorly and you'll be sorry you ever left the security of your backyard.

Chapter 5

Grizzly Bears:
Monarchs of the North Woods

There are no bigger, fiercer teeth on the continent than those belonging to the grizzly bear. This beast has instilled fear and humility into native peoples for eons. And European settlers have found it a daunting beast. The latter were introduced to grizzly bears by Meriwether Lewis and William Clark. These two explorers found many exciting, unexpected adventures during their two-year trek across the continent and back. It is said they exhibited undaunted courage in leading the legendary Corps of Discovery overland to the Pacific. But the mighty grizzly bear was the one creature that gave lie to the claim. In the unabridged journals of both captains and several of their men, which have been reproduced in an eleven-volume set, *The Journals of the Lewis and Clark Expedition,* it becomes clear that they found the grizzly an animal to be reckoned with.

While spending the winter of 1804-05 with the Mandan Indians on the banks of the Missouri River, the explorers were told of the ferocious nature of the great bears. The two captains failed to take the warning to heart. On April 29, 1805, shortly after leaving their winter quarters with the Mandans, the men in the Corps of Discovery came across their first grizzly bear.

Lewis writes of the event in his journal. He describes walking along the riverbank with another man from the party, when they encountered two bears. They fired their muzzle-loading rifles at the bears, wounding both of them. One immediately fled, but "the other," Lewis says, "after my firing on him pursued me seventy or eighty yards, but fortunately was so badly wounded that he was unable to pursue so close as to prevent my charging my gun; we again repeated our fire and killed him." This encounter convinced Lewis that the Mandans had overestimated the bears' abilities. "The Indians may well fear this animal equipped as they generally are with their bows and arrows . . . but in the hands of skillful riflemen, they are by no means as formidable or dangerous as they have been represented."

That opinion died quickly. In the next two weeks the Corps encountered many more bears, each proving difficult to kill, and very obstinate once wounded. In two back-to-back encounters, the first on May 11 and the second on May 14, 1805, the Corps ran into big male bears. These experiences finally convinced Lewis and Clark that the Indians had been quite accurate in their descriptions.

During the May 11th encounter, Lewis was again walking on the banks of the Missouri River when one of his men rushed up to him and excitedly told the captain he had shot a large bear, which instantly began to chase him. Lewis gathered up a few men and followed the hunter back to the bear's trail. They followed the bear's blood trail until they found the beast in some brush. It charged and they killed it with two rifle shots through the skull. They then discovered that the hunter's first shot had ripped open the bear's lungs. Even thus wounded, the beast had chased its attacker more than a mile and half through broken terrain, and still had enough strength to charge the team of hunters that Lewis led back to the scene. Lewis was amazed at the strength of will of the wounded bear, noting in his journal that the bear's "being so hard to die rather intimidates us all."

Three days later, Lewis was even more amazed. In his journal entry of May 14th, he notes that six of the crew members came across another grizzly. Four of them shot the bear from a distance of "about 40 paces." Again, the lungs were struck by bullets, but the bear charged the men, nonetheless. The two hunters who had held their fire during the first assault now fired, striking the bear in the shoulder and neck. The shoulder wound "retarded his motion for moment, but before they could reload he was so near that they were obliged to run to the river." The bear nearly caught them at the riverbank, but the men jumped into the water just ahead of the bear. Two leapt into a canoe while the other four separated and concealed themselves in the willows. From there, they fired as fast as each could reload. Lewis was clearly amazed. He says: "Each shot seemed only to direct him toward the hunter, till at last he pursued two of them so closely that they threw aside their guns and pouches, and jumped down a perpendicular bank of 20 feet into the river. The bear sprang after them and was within a few feet of the hindmost, when one of the hunters on shore shot him in the head and finally killed him. They dragged him to the shore and found that eight balls had passed through him in different directions."

After this encounter, the members of the Lewis and Clark corps afforded the great bears the respect they deserved. Indeed, their subsequent encounters led them to describe the bears as horrible and, again, "terribly hard to die." It was largely because of the accounts from Lewis and Clark that led George Ord in 1815 to assign the bears the formal name *Ursus horribilis,* or "horrible bear."

This view of the bears has been the prevalent view ever since. Nearly a century after Lewis and Clark first encountered the grizzly bear, Theodore Roosevelt, perhaps the greatest conservation president this country has ever had, called the bears "ghastly" and "horrifying." Today, grizzly bears are still among the most feared animals on the planet, despite the fact that they have been eradicated from most of their range. The fear undoubtedly stems from the fact that this is an animal that can kill and consume a human in a matter of minutes, that when we share the forests with grizzlies, we know we are not the top predator. In the northern forest, the mighty bruin *Ursus arctos horribilis* reigns supreme as the top predator south of the Arctic Circle. In the Arctic, the brown's pale cousin, the polar bear, *Ursus maritimus,* is lord of the manor.

Is the fear of the bears justified? To a degree, yes. But looking at the dangers calmly and rationally, it becomes apparent that there are far greater dangers facing us. Not that the bears are not dangerous. Certainly, grizzlies are enormously powerful and potentially deadly. But they are not naturally prone to rash, indiscriminate attacks. This becomes clear when we look at the experiences of the Corps of Discovery.

In 1804, when the explorers first encountered the brown bears and Lewis's men killed that first grizzly, the grizzly population was at its peak. After that year, the grizzly population began a slow but steady decline. It took a few years for the real killing to begin, but once the fur traders and trappers—"mountain men"—took to the Rockies, the bears became popular targets. So we can safely say there were more grizzly bears in the country traveled by Lewis and Clark than at any time since. A conservative estimate puts the number of grizzlies back then at about 50,000 bears. Yet the Corps of Discovery encountered just thirty-seven bears within a 1,000 mile section of their route (from the western section of the Great Plains to the area near the Snake River on the western slope of the Rockies). The fact that the explorers stayed close to the primary water source in that part of the plains, and that they hunted daily—thereby having plenty of blood and fresh meat to attract predators—would suggest that they saw more bears than more careful travelers might have. Still, thirty-seven sightings of grizzly bears in more than two years of trekking through prime grizzly habitat while the bear population was at its peak suggests that the bears weren't overly interested in meeting humans. Today, grizzlies are even less likely to approach humans— and far more likely to flee before humans ever see them—because they have learned that humans mean death.

Still, many folks, particularly wilderness recreationists, continue to harbor a deep-seated fear of encountering a grizzly bear, even when the odds of such an encounter are minuscule. On the other hand, many people feel a strong sense of respect and admiration for the great beasts, and some hikers and wilderness enthusiasts are actually excited about sharing the woods with the griz. This suggests to me that the bears are in the midst of a public relations makeover.

While the grizzly has suffered decades of exile from its historic range south of Canada (once, grizzly bears roamed as far south as the Sierra Madres of Mexico), the bears are slowly reclaiming a fraction of their former haunts in Washington, Idaho, Wyoming, and Montana. From a one-time population of more than 50,000 grizzlies in the western states, the continental United States now supports fewer than 1,000. This is to say that 98 percent of the population has been destroyed. Most of the remaining bears live in Yellowstone National Park in Montana and Wyoming and Glacier National Park in Montana. A few tiny, remnant populations struggle to survive in a handful of other isolated ecosystems, including Washington's North Cascades Ecosystem and the Selkirk Ecosystem between Idaho and Washington, along the Canadian border. The only other population of grizzly bears in the Lower 48 are in the Cabinet-Yaak Ecosystem straddling the Montana-Idaho-Canada borders, and the Bitterroot Ecosystem of central Idaho. That's it: There are just six isolated islands where the grizzly has survived, and this is confined to four western states.

The survival of this population is still in question, but there is some hope for the mighty bruins. Where humans once spent millions of dollars to eradicate the great bears, they are now trying to aid in their return to some areas.

The Endangered Species Act

Why the turnabout? Largely because of a piece of legislation signed into law in the early 1970s: the Endangered Species Act. In 1975, the grizzly bear was listed as a federally threatened species and, as such, it is required that the bears not only be left alone to rebuild their populations, but that plans be formulated and implemented to protect their dwindling habitat and to aid in their recovery when suitable habitat exists. The grizzly is also listed as an endangered species in Washington by the state Department of Wildlife, and the Canadian government has listed the grizzly bear as a vulnerable species.

In an effort to comply with the Endangered Species Act requirements, an Interagency Grizzly Bear Committee was established in 1983 to help the U.S. Fish and Wildlife Service (USFWS), which administers the Endangered Species Act, to identify the remaining grizzly habitat and current populations.

A recovery plan for the bears was developed in 1982, adopted in 1993, and amended in 1997 and 1999. That plan identified the six grizzly bear ecosystems—the North Cascades, Bitterroot, Selkirk, Yellowstone, Northern Continental Divide, and Cabinet-Yaak—in four western states.

The North Cascades Ecosystem includes all the North Cascades National Park Complex (including the Lake Chelan Recreation Area), all of Mount Baker-Snoqualmie and Wenatchee National Forests north of Interstate 90, and the Okanogan National Forest west of the Okanogan River. Within this 9,600-square-mile are, there are no more than fifty grizzlies; more likely there are probably only about fifteen or twenty. In the corresponding habitat north of the border in British Columbia, the grizzly population is roughly the same size—again, about fifteen or twenty bears. This is too few bears to be considered a viable population; there aren't enough bears to ensure that breeding-aged bears will be able to find mates and, even if they were to do so, the genetic pool may be too limited to sustain a population. Biologists aren't certain exactly how many bears would be needed to sustain a viable population, but the estimates are in the range of 200 to 400 in the U.S. recovery zone, and an equal number in the Canadian zone. Even by the most optimistic estimates, it would take a minimum of several decades to reach that level. Among the options for ensuring that the population will be increased are habitat protection, artificial insemination, and population augmentation—a process of strengthening the Washington population by moving a few young bears from a remote northern section of British Columbia to Washington.

The North Cascades and Bitterroot systems were the last to be evaluated and the last to go through the process of developing a recovery plan. The North Cascades Steering Committee finally published a draft version of the North Cascades Ecosystem Grizzly Bear Recovery Chapter in 1994, and approved a final plan in 1997. Because of lack of funding, the plan has never been implemented. Still the public has not been shy about responding to the draft plan. Two of the issues most frequently commented on are the potential augmentation of the grizzly bear population, and the possible closing of areas to recreational use to protect grizzly habitat.

There is also a vocal, if small, segment of the population that doesn't believe grizzly bears still exist. And a few insist, against all reason, that they never did exist in the North Cascades Ecosystem. They argue that because the bears are gone, we shouldn't bother trying to return them to the area; we should just accept that there are plenty of brown bears in Alaska and realize that we don't need to bring them back to "civilized" states. This "logic" flies in the face of the facts, which are supported by decades of field research and observation. The Interagency Grizzly Bear Commission (IGBC) confirmed more than twenty-two grizzly bear sightings in the recovery zone during a five-year study running 1986 through 1991. In the same study, the researchers chronicled eighty-two sightings that they classified as "highly reliable." That is, they fully believe these observations were of grizzly bears, but they have no concrete physical evidence to prove this is so.

More recently, biologists with the Northwest Ecosystem Alliance (NWEA) note that several reliable wilderness enthusiasts, including hunting guides, have reported sightings of grizzly sows with cubs in the northern sections of the recovery zone. NWEA, a nonprofit organization based in Bellingham, Washington, has been a leading proponent of grizzlies as well as other predators, and has been a strong voice for the protection of the ecosystems needed for the long-term survival of these wild animals.

On the augmentation issue, contrary to some speculations, no "problem bears" will be even considered for augmentation of the North Cascades population. The only bears that would even be considered for relocation to the North Cascades, should augmentation of the existing population be necessary, are sub-adult (two- to three-year-old) females that have had no prior contact with humans. These would likely be found in remote sections of British Columbia. In any North Cascades augmentation plan no more than twenty bears would be relocated, and it could take twenty years to relocate them all. In fact, augmentation has been tested in the Cabinet-Yaak Ecosystem and it took four years to find three suitable bears to augment that existing population.

Mitch Friedman, executive director of NWEA, points out that augmentation will be the only way to recover the bear population. "There just aren't any bears across the border that can get here. Natural recovery would require a protected migration corridor from a strong, stable bear population in Canada to the U.S. side of the border. That doesn't exist, and the population

just north of the border is in worse shape than the U.S. grizzly population."
Friedman would like to see the USFWS "get some guts" and implement a
real augmentation program that would work—a stable ten-year program of
augmenting the current population with strong young bears from Canada.
Beyond that, he says, the USFWS and the Interagency Grizzly Bear Commission must expand the existing recovery zone—it should be pushed south of
Interstate 90 at least as far as the Columbia River—and build habitat linkages to the Selkirk Ecosystem in the northeastern corner of Washington. In
fact, Friedman says, those linkages are key. He'd like to see all the six ecosystems linked by reasonable migration corridors, and he would also like to see
linkages to habitats in Canada.

Friedman sees the fight to protect the habitat as the key to wildlife issues. If animals' habitat is secure and safe, they can survive and thrive. The
most dire threats to the habitat are found north of the border. Canada is
clearcutting its forests at a rate that puts the U.S. timber harvest of the 1980s
to shame. As the forests fall to chainsaws, the endangered species of the
northern tier states in the United States lose the Canadian "seed populations" that have been supplementing and supporting them. The Canadian
habitat being cut is particularly bad news for the North Cascades because it
is the last significant area of low-elevation habitat in the ecosystem, and is
vital to the long-term health of many species, including the grizzlies. There
is little low-elevation habitat remaining in the U.S. portion of the North Cascades; it was developed as farm or ranch land long ago, and the areas that
haven't been converted to farm land have been logged and developed for
timber production.

Still, Friedman says, the prognosis for the wildlife habitat looks fairly
good. The U.S. Forest Service has nearly eliminated logging in the Mount
Baker-Snoqualmie National Forest, and has reduced the cut on the other
forests. With the 1999 decision by the Clinton Administration to enact a
moratorium on road-building on Forest Service Lands, the biggest threat to
the last intact blocks of wild lands has been halted, too. Bears, and other
solitude-loving wildlife such as a wolves, wolverines, and lynx, often abandon areas that have moderate to high road densities. By keeping the roads
from being built, and removing some of the roads that are no longer being
maintained (due to lack of funding and/or need), the necessary core habitat
is protected for these animals. But the road-building moratorium has another benefit—it prevents the extension of motorized recreation into the last
roadless areas.

Which leads into the other primary concern expressed by the people who have commented on the recovery plans: impact of the grizzly recovery on recreation. Some leaders in the hiking, horse packing, and climbing communities have been vocal opponents of grizzly recovery because they fear loss of recreational opportunities in the recovery zone. However, biologists with the IGBC note that it is highly unlikely any trails or recreational opportunities will be closed in the early phases of the bear's recovery. If and when trail closures are employed, they probably would be only for short periods—two weeks or less—and would be very localized. The primary reason for closures will be to keep recreationists and bears separate. For instance, if there is a female with cubs in a particular valley, the trails leading into the valley will be closed until the bears move on. And because bears only stay in an area as long as the foraging is good, they generally move on to fresh pastures within a week.

The NWEA research into impacts of grizzly habitat protection on recreation reveals that the concerns expressed by some hiking and horse groups are largely unfounded.

In trying to foresee what might happen in the North Cascades Ecosystems, we can look to some of the more established areas to see what impacts on recreation they have suffered. The NWEA compared the six ecosystems by measuring the Total Available Recreation Opportunity (TARO) and the percentage of that TARO lost to grizzly recovery plans. They issued a comprehensive report on this subject in 1994. The report shows that the greatest loss of recreational opportunity has occurred in Yellowstone National Park, which lost about 4 percent of its TARO in 1993. Glacier National Park, the second most impacted ecosystem (and, incidentally, the ecosystem with the second largest density of grizzlies, behind Yellowstone), lost about 1.3 percent of its TARO each of the previous six years.

This doesn't mean that 4 percent of wilderness recreationists in Yellowstone were turned away. Rather, the "percentage of TARO lost" refers to lost potential recreational opportunities. That is, 100 percent of the people who wish to recreate in Yellowstone could still do so, but the trails, campgrounds, and fishing areas available to them were reduced by 4 percent during the year. Bear in mind also that Yellowstone represents the higher end of the scale. The NWEA report notes that the average lost TARO for all the grizzly bear zones was a mere 0.5 percent annually.

Again, this doesn't mean that one out of every 200 forest visitors is sent home because of lost recreational opportunities. Rather, it shows that only half of 1 percent of all the trails, roads, and/or campgrounds—the total rec-reational options in the forests—are closed at some time during the year. So at any given time, there is still 99.5 percent of the recreational opportunities available to the public. Should there be a closure of a trail for a week or two, then, 99.5 percent of the trails in the district are still open to recreation. This may create a minor, temporary, inconvenience. But in reality, it affects a tiny minority of people.

Most of the lost TARO isn't the result of trail closures, however, but of road closures. In some cases, there have been severe reductions in the num-ber of road miles left open within selected ranger districts in the heart of recovery zones. In the Kootenai National Forest, for instance, the road in-ventory was reduced from a whopping 7,000 miles of roads to just over 2,500 miles—a reduction of 40 percent. That is the most extreme example, but road closures will likely occur to some degree in each of the grizzly recovery zones, although, to date, the Custer and Beaverhead National Forests in Montana and Wyoming have had no road closures in their portions of the bear zones.

The protection of the bear habitat in the recovery zones will certainly require closures of some forest roads. On the surface, this looks as if it could be devastating to hikers and horseback riders: If the roads are closed, how do we get to the trailheads? Not to worry, though. A deeper look at the road closures that have taken place in other ecosystems that are further along in the planning process shows that the majority of closed roads are redundant and of no importance to hikers. That is, many of the roads the Forest Service has built over the years traverse the same landscape, and are designed sim-ply to provide fast, easy access for logging trucks to all aspects of a logged area. Many of the redundant roads run parallel to each other, separated by less than a quarter of a mile—and usually no more than a couple hundred yards. Closing these types of roads actually improves recreation in the area because it minimizes noise, dust, and erosion along the trails and roads that are left in place. Also, the closed roads are off-limits to motorized vehicles (except snowmobiles) but remain open to mountain bikes, horses, hikers, cross-country skiers, snowshoers, and trail runners. So the road closures, when they happen, will affect motorized recreationists—motorcyclists, ORV riders, four-wheel-drive enthusiasts, etc.—more than muscle-powered recreationists.

Then we get to the fact that the Forest Service has a huge backlog of road maintenance projects that likely will never get fully funded by Con-gress. Indeed, the Mount Baker–Snoqualmie National Forest had more than

3,000 miles of inventoried roads in 1994 but received allocations for maintenance and annual upkeep for fewer than 500 miles. The roads are literally disintegrating and are causing all kinds of problems, from slope erosion and sedimentation of salmon-bearing streams to leading casual forest visitors into dangerous situations.

I believe that hikers, horse packers, and mountain bikers—perhaps mountain bikers most of all—will actually benefit from these methodical closures of redundant and obsolete roads. Mountain bikers will find they have literally thousands of miles of narrow dirt track to explore, unmolested by motorized vehicles. Hikers will have fewer chances of getting lost after straying off onto the wrong road when driving to a remote trailhead, and they will have few roads intersecting their lowland trails. And horse packers will enjoy greater freedom of choice when they head for the woods: They can choose between an easy ride along a closed road and a tough but rewarding trip up a single-track trail.

Beyond the road closures, another likely impact of the recovery plans will be felt by commercial outfitters and guides. These folks, who profit from use of the public lands, have been subjected to greater restrictions and licensing requirements in other ecosystems, but not a single outfitter or guide has been put out of business by the grizzly plans. Indeed, some have been able to jack up the price of their services because of perceived added danger/thrill (this depends on how they market themselves) in venturing out into grizzly country. The restrictions the guides have endured—and sometimes been vocally opposed to—have included requirements for safer food handling in camp. In other words, guides and outfitters were required to keep clean camps, and to store all food items in a bear-safe manner every night, just as the average hiker is required to do. I'm not sure why the guides would object to this regulation, but I suspect it is simply because they don't like the inconvenience of suspending ice chests full of food in trees, nor do they appreciate cooking outside their camps. But these practices, which are followed by every responsible backpacker in bear country, must be followed by commercial users, too. By doing so, guides will not only keep their clients safe, they will also help protect every other hiker and wilderness user who comes along after them. Perhaps, too, the guides are objecting to those regulations because they fear greater restrictions on their activities down the road. This may be a valid concern: Some forests in grizzly bear recovery zones have enacted moratoriums on issuing new guide licenses, and others have banned the development of new backcountry camps for these commercial outfitters.

Keep in mind that an outfitter's camp, especially in remote country like the Pasayten Wilderness, requires space for several large canvas tents (8 or 10 feet square), a pole corral for the horses, a large meadow for grazing. These aren't the camps envisioned by the designers of the Leave No Trace practices.

While these restrictions have limited the cash flow potential for some outfitters, they certainly improve business for others. And, individual hikers and horse packers—the folks who head out on trails without the services of a professional guide/cook/camp host—will benefit greatly by the restriction on commercial use. There will be fewer large groups to impact their solitude and wilderness setting. There will be fewer developed sites that mar the landscape, and there will be more opportunities to use areas where use is restricted for administrative or environmental reasons. That is, if the Forest Service only allows twenty-five people to start up a trail on any given day, and twenty of those are using a commercial guide service, that leaves just five spots for folks who want to "do it on their own." By restricting the guides' access, land managers increase individuals' recreational opportunities.

The potential loss of recreational opportunities in the North Cascades Ecosystem doesn't seem to be a valid concern, given what has been occurring in other Grizzly Bear Recovery Zones. I believe there will be some impact, both positive and negative, for the average forest visitor, but on a whole the average trail user—of the non-motorized variety—will actually benefit from the grizzly bear's recovery. Not only will there be essentially as much recreational opportunity as there is today, the quality of the wilderness itself will be better, with fewer roads, fewer developments, and more wildness. More wildness because simply adding grizzlies—even two or three—to an ecosystem makes it a wild and fearsome place. And that primal feeling of fear we feel when thinking about grizzly bears—the same instinctive fear felt by Captains Lewis and Clark and their men—is the essence of the wilderness.

The Bear Facts: The Life and Times of a Grizzly Bear

At birth, a grizzly bear is smaller than a chipmunk and more helpless than a jellyfish on the beach. At 21 to 25 ounces, newborn cubs are tiny, fragile creatures. The tiny and un-bearlike newborn cubs actually gave rise to one of our oldest cliches. According to European folklore, bear cubs are born as misshapen blobs. The mother bear then licks it incessantly until it is formed into the shape of a bear cub. That is, the sow takes the cub and "licks it into shape."

Of course, the cub is a bear all along, and the mother's licking is merely a means to keep the cub clean and warm during the last months of hibernation. For the cubs are born midwinter while the sows are huddled in their hibernation dens. So the cubs usually have three or four months to open their eyes, put on some weight, grow a fur coat, and develop an intense sense of curiosity. By the time they leave the cozy den, grizzly cubs weigh around 9 pounds and resemble cute, cuddly teddy bears.

For all its cuteness, though, the cub's chances of living to see its first birthday are just barely better than even. More than 40 percent of all grizzly cubs are killed before the age of one. The cause of death ranges from disease to accidents to predation by cougars or even by male grizzlies to not putting on enough fat to survive a long winter of hibernation.

Because grizzly cubs are often preyed upon by male bears or other predator species, sows have developed a fierce sense of protection over their youngsters. When they are trying to defend their cubs or their feeding territory, grizzlies are intimidating to say the least. Faster than a quarter horse on a track, grizzlies don't slow down much when they are running through broken forest or up hills. There are confirmed reports of bears running more than 41 miles per hour through downed timber. Once they attack, they employ 3- to 4-inch claws, 1- to 2-inch canine teeth and incredible strength. But despite the fierce bond with mother and child and the sows' protective instincts, many cubs still die from accident or disease.

That high cub mortality rate is one reason grizzly bear populations are slow to recover after a large reduction in numbers. Depending on the habitat and availability of food in the region, cubs may be born with one or two siblings. In the North Cascades, the habitat generally supports small litters of just one or two cubs.

Females don't breed until they are four and a half years old and have only one litter every three to four years after that. Although cubs appear to be fully grown by their second spring, they generally stay with their mothers throughout their second year and den with her again that winter, not leaving home until they are two and a half years old.

In the North Cascades and Rocky Mountains, grizzly males grow to an average weight of 350 to 400 pounds, while an adult female weighs about 250 pounds. In northern Canada and Alaska, grizzlies (known in those locales simply as brown bears) can exceed 1,500 pounds! By comparison, the American black bear averages 200 to 250 pounds for an adult male and 100 to 150 pounds for an adult female. Standing upright, a male grizzly bear can be 7 feet tall. And Alaskan brown bears can tower an amazing 9 to 10 feet on their hind legs. These massive beasts have a life expectancy of fifteen to twenty years, though many die before they are ten years old.

Besides their greater size, grizzly bears differ from black bears in a number of ways. Most observable differences are somewhat subtle and can be missed in the adrenaline-filled moments of an encounter. Both species can be a variety of colors, from light tan (almost white) to glossy black, so color is not a good way to differentiate between them. A better visual clue is the bear's back. Grizzly bears, both male and female, have a prominent hump on their back at the shoulders. They also have much larger claws that are straight, with the ends of the claws sitting close to the pads of their feet; black bears have shorter, more curved claws. If you're lucky, you'll be using this method to differentiate between the different types of bears from their tracks. If you are making this analysis from the claws themselves, you are way, WAY too close to the bears!

Another difference is that black bears tend to have longer, pointed noses and faces—their foreheads and cheeks slope in a smooth, direct line out along the snout to the nose—while grizzlies have a concave, or "dish-shaped" face. The area around a grizzly's eyes and forehead is concave, with its snout protruding from the base of the dish.

A beast the size of a grizzly bear requires a good deal of land to support its endless hunger. On average, females occupy a home range of 50 to 300 square miles, while males patrol some 200 to 500 square miles. These aren't exclusive territories—they tend to overlap with the home ranges of other grizzlies, but they typically have a core range of various sizes that they protect as their individual space. A grizzly occupies a variety of vegetation and landscape types in its travels, and it needs each of the ecosystem types it patrols, from deep, old forests to alpine and subalpine meadows to valley bottom grasslands and riverbeds.

Though their reputation is that of a fierce, remorseless killer, grizzly bears are omnivores and do most of their feeding on berries, roots, and grasses. But they are very opportunistic and will take advantage of any available meat source, including winter-killed deer and elk. They rarely act as aggressive predators. This is not to say they can't and won't, but a grizzly that chases down and kills a deer for food is the exception, not the rule. Grizzlies will, however, take advantage of any opportunity to prey on young, defenseless deer, elk, and even bear cubs.

Studies of grizzly bears in each of the six recovery zones show that the bears' diet consists of 90 to 95 percent plant matter, and just 5 to 10 percent meat. Berries, roots, and grass were the primary foods of choice, although it was also found the bears frequently caught and consumed worms, ants, maggots, other insects and their larvae, and small rodents. Grizzly bears are often seen tearing apart dead, decaying trees in order to get access to the ant colonies and other hordes of insects within the rotting wood. They are voracious eaters, and because they only feed for six or eight months each year, they must eat vast quantities. One adult bear can decimate a huckleberry, salmonberry, or blueberry crop in a matter of hours. The U.S. Fish and Wildlife Service (USFWS), in trying to explain the bear's appetite, notes that an adult male grizzly bear can consume the caloric equivalent of ten huckleberry pies every day during the height of berry season. That, of course, is often followed by a "desert" course that might consist of a tree full of boring beetles or a mound of ants.

That's just in August. By September, grizzlies begin to feed with a vengeance, perhaps realizing that their time is limited before they have to crawl in their dens for a long winter. They become eating machines, feeding for as many as twenty hours each day. Some bears in Yellowstone have been reported to gain an average of 3 pounds a day during this last-minute feeding frenzy. All told, during the summer and autumn feeding, grizzlies can pack on an extra 100 or more pounds before returning to the den to sleep it off.

A grizzly den is almost always above 6,000 feet elevation. Here they will be safe from seasonal variations in weather; at 6,000 feet there is always a heavy, constant snowpack until spring. Though they will on occasion utilize available natural caves, most bears dig a den into a hillside or under a tree's roots. They'll burrow at least 6 feet deep, chewing through any roots that get in their way and rolling rocks of up to 100 or 150 pounds easily out of the way. Digging a den takes a lot of work, yet bears seldom use the same den site twice. They prefer to dig a fresh den each year. Or rather, most bears do. Like humans, not all bears are industrious. There are lazy grizzlies, just as there are lazy humans. These sluggard bears can't be bothered with digging a den—they have been observed simply crawling into a tangle of bushes and going to sleep, essentially letting the winter's snow pile up around them, forming a "snow cave" den.

Grizzlies will stay in hibernation for six or seven months. Or rather, they will stay inside the den that long. While they are idle all winter, theirs is not a true hibernation; they don't literally sleep the entire winter. Grizzlies awaken on occasion and may even come out of the den for a day or two if the weather is warm.

In the spring, adult males typically leave the dens first. They are generally heavier and aren't as pressed to begin gorging themselves immediately upon waking up, so they can venture out before the berries and grasses are in full supply.

Females with cubs are generally the last to leave the dens. It is important for them to make sure the cubs are old enough and strong enough to travel and, because of the extra drain on their fat reserves (from providing milk to the cubs), mothers must have an ample supply of food readily available once they leave the den. So it pays for them to sleep a few weeks longer until the grasses are long and rich.

How Humans View the Grizzly Bear

Native cultures throughout the northern hemisphere have historically revered and respected brown bears. The tale of humans and bears originating from the Great Mother Bear is common to many cultures in North America and Asia.

Doug Peacock, author of *Grizzly Years*, may have spent more time with wild U.S. grizzlies than any other living person. He has been filming grizzlies in the remotest regions of northern Montana, Wyoming, Canada, and Alaska since 1973. In his book, Peacock says that "to the ancient Blackfeet the grizzly, whom they called Real Bear, was the most esteemed of all animals." He also notes that the thirty-seven bears killed by Lewis and Clark's crew was just the start of the killing that would eventually exterminate the beasts in most of their natural territories.

The slaughter of the grizzly bear in the western states was not unlike the destruction of other species—wolves, bison, passenger pigeons, etc. Individuals settlers acted to clear and protect their portion of the vast western landscape, and groups of farmers and ranchers acted together to eliminate those animals capable of preying on their livestock. So grizzlies were hit with both loss of habitat and an active extermination program. The cumulative effect was a reduction in grizzly population of 98 percent, a reduction of the wolf population to a fraction of 1 percent, and the reduction of passenger pigeons to a footnote in the history books and few stuffed specimens in museums.

But grizzlies are also different from the rest. Grizzlies were the one beast that didn't especially fear humans and that were capable of killing and eating humans. That gave the farmers, ranchers and townspeople who settled the West a bit more of a personal stake in the move to eradicate grizzlies.

Bears were killed for the simple reason that they evoked fear in people. Fur traders started the all-out war on grizzlies in the 1810s as they moved West into the Rocky Mountains to begin the American fur trading business. They killed the bears on sight, simply to kill them. They occasionally took the hide for trade with native peoples, but more often they merely took the liver or heart for their dinner meal and left the rest of the bear to rot. They killed because they feared the bears would kill them if left to roam the woods freely. That merciless assault on grizzlies continued into the late twentieth century, until the bears were either entirely wiped out in an area or decimated to the point where their future was seriously in jeopardy.

Now that the bears have been gone for a while—the last grizzly bear in California was killed in 1922, the last in Oregon died in 1931, the final death in Arizona came in 1935, and one holdout in Colorado lasted until 1979— attitudes are slowly changing. Bears are returning from Canada, and while their return is controversial, laws protecting the immigrating grizzlies are ensuring their future here.

Although the danger of hiking in a wilderness area containing grizzlies is statistically less than the danger of hiking across a cattle ranch, the idea of grizzly bears being "out there" evokes an instinctive rush of fear and adrenaline. That "rush" will cause some to abandon plans to recreate in bear habitat, but that same burst of adrenaline and unease will draw others to those wilderness areas.

Those who decide to hike in bear country will do well to learn a few simple guidelines to further increase their chances of avoiding an unpleasant encounter.

What to Do in an Encounter with a Griz

Doug Peacock has been charged by grizzlies more than forty times and has never been mauled or even scratched. After two decades of observing and interacting with wild grizzlies, Peacock notes that "grizzlies virtually never assault people without provocation. The exceptions to this rule—and they are exceedingly rare—are apparent predatory attacks." Grizzly bear attacks on humans are almost always the result of the people blundering in upon a bedded or feeding grizzly at very close range, or by stumbling upon a cub that has wandered away from momma. These types of encounters may elicit a reflexive charge from the bear that results in a mauling. But, Peacock says, even when a grizzly charges, it doesn't necessarily mean it is attacking. The bear may simply be testing you to see how you react. During the charge, the bear will decide whether to follow through on the attack, or call it off as a bluff. Often, it's what you do that makes up the grizzly's mind for him.

The basic idea, most grizzly bear experts agree, is that you must show the grizzly your intentions are peaceful without showing docility or weakness. Remain still, standing upright, with arms partially raised to increase your apparent body size. Be as inoffensive as possible, while offering some sign that you are also somewhat defensive (for example, avoid direct eye contact). Don't make sudden movements or loud noises. This includes hollering and waving.

The leading cause of grizzly bear attacks and maulings is the result of people running and trying to climb trees. The fact that a grizzly can outrun a quarter horse should convince you that it is too late to climb a tree once the bear is aware of you. The simple process of you running overturns whatever thought the bear might have had of leaving you alone and triggers an instinctive move to attack. It's the predator-prey instinct at work, and there are thousands of years of evolution working against you if it kicks in.

If you are attacked by a grizzly, the best way to ensure your survival is to play dead after the bear hits you. Lie on your belly with your head covered by your arms and don't move. If the bear tries to flip you over, roll with it and keep rolling until you are back on your belly (this protects your vital organs from the beast).

Typically, a grizzly will leave a human alone once it is convinced you are no longer a threat. This behavior differs from that of black bears, which typically try to eat anyone they attack. As detailed in this book's chapter about black bears, the recommended behavior for black bears is to fight back if attacked—kick, punch, gouge its eyes, whatever. But when a grizzly attacks, continue to play dead.

Government biologists and wildlife management folks have several suggestions for avoiding an encounter before you have to deal with a potential attack situation. The following are some of their recommendations.

- ◆ Pitch your tent 100 yards uphill from the area where you're cooking and storing your food.
- ◆ Store only sleeping gear and clean clothing in the tent. Never sleep in the clothing you wore while cooking.
- ◆ Never use the stuff sacks for tents or sleeping bags to store food, garbage, cooking gear, or cosmetics. This may transmit these smells that are attractive to bears to tents and sleeping bags.
- ◆ Never cook in or near the tent.

- ◆ Avoid cooking strong-smelling foods and use dehydrated foods when possible.
- ◆ Use a stove instead of a cooking fire whenever possible.
- ◆ Hang all food, garbage, cooking gear, and cosmetics in a tree at least 10 feet above the ground and 4 feet from the tree truck or nearby branches. Use PVC-type float sacks for storing such items to minimize odors.
- ◆ Never bury or burn garbage.
- ◆ If dogs are permitted in the area, keep your dog on a leash; a free-ranging dog may lead a bear back to you.

Putting the Wild Back in Wilderness

I've never seen a grizzly bear in the wilds, but having hiked in grizzly country, I can tell you there is a tangible difference between those wild areas and wildernesses that don't harbor brown bears and those that do. The excitement, apprehension, and thrill that bubbles up from the core of your being when sharing the woods with the great bears is the heart and soul of the wilderness.

I am an avid hiker and have no wish to reduce my wilderness recreation opportunities. Yet I will happily give up a remote trail or two for short periods of time if it means that the grizzlies have a chance to return in stable numbers to the wild lands of Washington. Those grizzlies provide wildness to the wilderness. They ensure that humans aren't merely visitors to the backcountry, but participants. When the griz roams the woods, humans must actively monitor their own activities and balance their actions against the actions of the bears. In other words, we must do things not as we wish but as the bears dictate we should. If we fail to make those accommodations to the bears—if we cook in our tents, fail to keep a clean camp, and neglect to hang our food—we risk becoming even more actively involved with the wildest of the wild beasts.

I, for one, will strive to keep my distance from the grizzlies, but I hope it's not such a great distance that I can't observe the bears. Seeing a grizzly bear lumbering through a subalpine meadow in the Central Cascades would be the ultimate sign to me that our wildernesses are strong and enduring. I believe that eventually I will see this sight. I hope you can see it, too.

Chapter 6

Wolves: The Social Predators

To visit a wilderness area is to expose your senses to wild stimuli. There is the pungent smell of conifers and wildflowers, the feel of chilling winds, the sensation of the searing sun and biting insects, and the sounds of choruses of wild animals and birds: the whistle of marmots, the scream of hawks, the teetering of songbirds, the chirp of insects.

All are sounds of the wilderness, yet no sound is wilder, no sound evokes such a primal feeling of wildness, than the deep, soulful howl of the wolf. The great American conservationist and natural history writer, Aldo Leopold, wrote in 1949 in *A Sand Country Almanac* that to understand the wild lands and the mountains, we must learn to think like a mountain. For, he says, "only the mountain has lived long enough to listen objectively to the howl of a wolf."

Leopold recounts how, during a trip to the wildernesses of Arizona and New Mexico, he came to appreciate and respect the wolf. In his youth, he had bought into the idea that the elimination of wolves from the wilderness was a good thing; with no wolves, there would be more deer for him and other hunters like him. So when he and his companions spotted an old, female wolf with a handful of young pups crossing a creek, they immediately unslung their rifles and opened fire. The wolves instantly scattered, but the riflemen managed to cripple one pup and mortally wound the female. As they approached, the wolf died before their eyes. "We reached the old wolf in time to watch a fierce green fire dying in her eyes. I realized then, and have known ever since, that there is something new to me in those eyes— something known only to her and to the mountain." Leopold never again raised his rifle toward a wolf, and sought to prevent others from doing so as well. His efforts came too late, however. Wolves disappeared from state after state during the 1910s, '20s and '30s.

Leopold mourned their loss, for he saw it as a loss of wildness in the wilderness. Even if we can't understand the deeper meanings of the howls, he reasoned, we can feel its power: "Those unable to decipher the hidden meaning know nevertheless that it is there, for it is felt in all wolf country, and distinguishes that country from all other lands." This sound has been absent from most wild areas of the United States, including Washington, for several decades. Now, after the animals' long exile, the Cascades may echo once more with the howl of wolves, further distinguishing the wildernesses of Washington from other, less wild country.

The Life of a Wolf

In any given wolf pack, the dominant male and the dominant female—the alpha animals—are the only breeding pair. After the late winter or early spring breeding period, the female seeks a den. Frequently, dens are used year after year by the same pack, even when new alpha females take over. One den in Alaska that has been studied extensively by Adolph Murie, the noted American biologist and naturalist, is still in use fifty years after it was first found.

Once settled into the den, the mother-to-be prepares for birth, which comes sixty-three days after mating. Litters range in size from three to nine pups and average four or five. Weighing just one pound at birth, the pups are blind, deaf, and virtually immobile for a couple of weeks. But it doesn't take long for the feeble newborns to become curious explorers; just three weeks after birth, the pups are romping outside the den.

By their ninth week, the pups are big and strong enough to move with the pack to a "rendezvous site," which is merely a home above ground where the pack congregates to socialize, sleep, and feed between hunting forays. By fall, the pups, like human teens, are often adult-sized but still lack adult skill and abilities. During the winter, when the pack has to range far and wide in search of food, the youngsters come of age and learn to hunt and contribute to the pack. The pups are nearly full grown when they are seven or eight months old, but remain with the pack at least until their second year.

At age two or three years old, the pups have reached their full maturity and are ready to mate. Some of these young adults remain with the pack, but others set off on their own—either on their own terms, or because they have challenged the pack's alpha wolf of their sex and were defeated in their coup attempt. These lone wolves disperse out of the pack's home range, looking for a new territory in which they can establish their own pack. Or, they might seek out another pack with a weaker alpha animal that they can displace. Regardless, these "dispersers" often travel more than 500 miles at times in their search for a new home. These loners have been known to travel 125 miles in a day. The greatest recorded dispersal distance for a wolf on the lookout for new territory is more than 800 miles. That explains why former residents of British Columbia and Ontario have been seen and heard as far south as the Columbia River and Yellowstone National Park.

When on the move, wolves can lope along at five to nine miles per hour all day long. Wolves are tireless runners. Barry Lopez, in his book *Of Wolves and Men*, notes that the animals are often on the move for eight to ten hours every day. Adolph Murie reported that a pack he was observing in Alaska made a regular daily circuit of 40 miles in search of food. During a hunt, the animals can maintain speeds of 25 miles per hour for upwards of 20 minutes and can exceed 45 miles per hour for short bursts. Wolf packs establish home ranges that they regularly patrol and defend from strange wolves, cougars, and coyotes. Especially coyotes; wolves will try to kill any coyote they see. These territories range in size from 50 square miles in wooded areas with lots of prey to more than 1,000 square miles on the plains and the tundra, where prey herds are more disbursed. As they leap toward their prey, wolves can cover more than 16 feet in a single bound. And, when they catch something, they exert 1,500 pounds of pressure per square inch with their jaws.

Adult wolves weigh in somewhere between 50 and 100 pounds (occasionally, males can reach 150 pounds), with the females being about 20 percent lighter than the males. Measured from the tip of the tail to the end of the snout, male wolves can be 6 feet long or more and stand 30 inches tall at the shoulder.

Of their senses, their vision is the least developed—though that's not to say it isn't excellent. But their hearing and sense of smell is much more important to their lives. Wolves can hear others howling at distances of 6 to 10 miles away. Their sense of smell has been estimated to be several hundred times better than that of humans. Biologists have recorded incidents where wolves have scented prey that was a mile and a half away. They are said to be able to pick individual scents out of a jumble of hundreds of odors.

This all adds up to help make the wolf a highly efficient hunter. So efficient that, even though these animals have been driven from much of the United States, they are finding ways to return to take advantage of the unfilled predator niche in many locales.

The Family Unit

To understand why wolves are returning to the continental United States, it's important to understand the lifestyles of the animal.

Note the plural form of the word "lifestyles." That is important because it is difficult to generalize about how wolves live. Though a structured pack is the norm, the number of members in wolf packs varies widely, as does the social structure of the pack.

Perhaps the easiest generalization to make about wolves is that they are social animals and usually seem to revel in the company of their pack mates.

When members of a pack are separated for a time, for whatever reason, their reunion is joyous and boisterous with much playful romping, nipping, and barking.

This socialization is vital to the long-term health of the pack, as the primary food of wolves is large hoofed animals. Because adult wolves are generally smaller than their prey, the success of their hunting depends on teamwork.

The pack is not only a hunting team, though. It is a close family unit. Often the smaller packs that inhabit the Cascades and Rockies comprise six or seven members of the same immediate family—usually two parents and three or four offspring and maybe an uncle or aunt. Packs further north generally are larger simply because their prey is larger—moose and caribou as opposed to the deer and elk preyed on around the U.S. border—and requires more hunters to bring down.

In the typical pack, only the dominant male and female, again, called the alpha pair, breeds. But the entire pack takes on the responsibility of raising the young. Aunts and uncles may babysit while the parents are away or napping, and all the adults play with and teach the youngsters. In fact, the adults often seem to delight in their playtime with pups.

The Politics of Wolf Life

Just over two decades ago, any wolf that ventured south of the border into Washington, Idaho, Montana, or Minnesota was doomed. The same fate that befell the native packs hit these emigrants: poison, traps, or bullets—usually subsidized or paid for directly by the U. S. government. State and federal governments began paying bounties for dead wolves as far back as the 1600s in North America (this type of bounty was one of the first government programs to be transplanted to this continent from Europe) and continued until the wolves all disappeared, or, in those few areas where small populations survived, until the passage of the Endangered Species Act in 1973. The wolf was one of the first species to be listed as endangered.

Small populations of gray wolves were protected around Glacier National Park in Wyoming, in northwestern Minnesota, and on Isle Royale in Lake Superior just off the Minnesota shore. Even smaller populations of the shy, elusive red wolf were protected and monitored in the coastal areas of Texas and Louisiana. Unfortunately for the species, the protection was too little, too late. The red wolf was declared extinct in the wild in 1980.

Still, there are red wolves in existence, thanks to the efforts of captive breeding programs. A program for red wolves was begun in the early 1970s. More than 400 wild red wolves were collected before the wild populations disappeared. After a shaky start (at one point the world population of red wolves had plummeted to seventeen animals) the captive breeding program, managed by Point Defiance Zoo in Tacoma, proved to be a success, and red wolves were reintroduced into selected areas around 1987. Between 1987 and 1992, thirty-six captive-born red wolves were released into the Alligator National Refuge. At least twenty-one have died and the future of the animal in the wild is still up in the air.

The gray wolf is in better shape. When the animal was listed as endangered under the Endangered Species Act, the U.S. Fish and Wildlife Service (USFWS) developed a recovery plan for the existing populations of wolves. As this book is being written the Northern Rocky Mountain Recovery Plan is up for revision and, because there have been a number of confirmed sighting and howlings of wolves in Washington State, the Cascades will be included in some fashion in the revised recovery plan.

Steve Fritts, Northern Rocky Mountain Wolf Recovery Coordinator for the USFWS, says planning is underway to find the best way to deal with any population of wolves in Washington. One likely scenario is to develop a North Cascades or Washington Chapter for the revised recovery plan, similar to the grizzly bear plan that was implemented.

"Washington will certainly be given serious consideration in the future recovery of the wolf," Fritts says, "but there isn't a great deal of urgency to the planning right now. If there were a sizable population there now, we would have to act quickly to protect it, but what I see happening is a slow natural recolonization process in the Cascades."

Jeff Haas, a wildlife biologist with the USFWS office in Olympia, notes there have been several confirmed sightings of wolves in the Cascades in the late 1980s and early 1990s. There have also been wolf sightings south of Interstate 90 in the past, but there haven't been many sightings or howlings in the last couple years. Much of the field work of locating and documenting resident wolves is done by biologists and volunteer "howling brigades." These volunteer groups are generally organized and led by nonprofit organizations, such as Wolf Haven International, in Tenino. They travel to mountain ridges and passes and howl like wolves. Most wolf researchers will agree that if there is anything that wolves like to do more than travel, it's to howl, so any wild wolf within ear shot, which can be 5 or 10 miles for wolves, will generally howl in response.

Any recovery effort will be a long, drawn-out affair. But it can happen. It has happened. While there are no plans to reintroduce wolves into the North Cascades—the USFWS continues to hold out hopes that "disperser" wolves will naturally recolonize the Cascades—there are plans under way to return wolves to the Olympic Peninsula. Because the Peninsula is an isolated land mass with no hope of natural recovery, any return of the wolf there will have to follow the example set in the 1990s by the recovery programs in the Greater Yellowstone Ecosystem and the Central Idaho Ecosystem.

The Northern Rocky Mountains Model

The public perception of wolves has been evolving over the last few decades, and the greatest sign of the new attitude came a few years ago in Montana and Idaho. In 1995 and 1996, the USFWS brought more than sixty wolves to remote sections of Yellowstone National Park and the wildernesses of central Idaho. Thirty-one of the wolves were released into huge pens in Yellowstone, and thirty-five were penned in an enclosure in the remote mountain country of Idaho. The wolves stayed in the huge enclosures for several months as they acclimated to the local climate and environment. Then, in 1996, the wolves were released into the wild to multiply and prosper. The wolves weren't entirely free—the alpha animals in each group were collared with radio transmitters, and the movements of the packs were followed by biologists on the ground and in the air for the next several years. Still, the wolves enjoyed their return to their ancestral ranges and have prospered indeed.

The reintroduction of these wolves to their former haunts was a slow and convoluted process. The wolves were exterminated from the Yellowstone Ecosystem by the 1930s, and there was no interest in bringing the animals back until the 1970s, when public attitudes toward wilderness and wildlife were undergoing a dramatic shift. In 1972, the U.S. Department of Interior, which manages the National Park Service, organized a meeting of biologists, bureaucrats, and park managers, among others, to discuss wolf restoration in Yellowstone. That inaugural meeting ended with a decision that the Park Service should conduct a study to confirm that wolves were indeed extinct in the park. The findings surprised no one: Wolves were indeed missing from Yellowstone and the adjacent lands. By 1980, the federal government, with the USFWS acting as the lead agency, developed plans to recover gray wolves throughout the northern Rocky Mountains. That plan sat on the shelves for years with little or no work being done to implement it.

After several environmental organizations and individuals pushed for more action, the wolf recovery plan was revised in 1987, at which time the Yellowstone, Central Idaho, and Northwest Montana Ecosystems, i.e., Glacier National Park and adjoining lands—were specifically noted as recovery zones for the endangered wolf. The recovery plans finally saw some action, slow though it was, and by 1992, Congress had stepped in and issued a directive to the various federal agencies—the USFWS, Forest Service, and National Park Service—to develop an environmental impact statement (EIS) for the reintroduction of wolves into Yellowstone. For more than two years, the agencies conducted research, held public meetings, and compiled the data into the EIS, which was made public in 1994. More than 160,000 public comments were incorporated into the EIS, illustrating the degree to which the public was interested in the wolf plan.

By the summer of 1994, just months after the final EIS was published, the U.S. Departments of Agriculture, and Interior (which manage the Forest Service and National Park Service, respectively) had accepted the EIS findings, and the Secretaries of Agriculture and Interior endorsed plans to reintroduce wolves to the specified ecosystems.

The need to reintroduce the wolves, rather than merely wait while they returned on their own from adjacent habitats in Canada, was explained as the only viable way to make sure a strong, stable population of healthy wolves was returned to the ecosystems.

Yet, even with the approval of the new cabinet secretaries, the transplanting of wolves from Canada or Alaska was seen as a drastic action, and it faced vocal public opposition. To smooth the public concerns, the USFWS decided to take advantage of a 1982 change in the Endangered Species Act that allowed the agency to manage "experimental" population of endangered species.

That designation of experimental population allows agencies involved to be more flexible in their plans by lifting some of the strict restrictions that the full protection of the Endangered Species Act imposes on development, accidental kills of listed species, and the removal of certain problem individuals (i.e., individual animals that prey on domestic livestock or pose a threat to humans). This was done to help mitigate and minimize problems and conflicts with the people whom the reintroductions would affect most: the neighboring landowners.

To get a population of endangered animals listed as an experimental population, the USFWS must prepare a list of regulations, or, more specifically, a list of approved actions and prohibited actions concerning that population. The purpose of this is to define the procedures the local governments and landowners can take (or cannot take) when they encounter wolves. The hope is that by establishing the reintroduced wolves as an experimental population, rather than as a natural population, the disruptions of the local economies and social programs of the nearby communities and residents will be minimized.

In the Greater Yellowstone Ecosystem, the USFWS developed the following regulations (also known as the Final Rule of the experimental population):

◆ State and tribal wildlife agencies are encouraged to lead wolf recovery efforts outside national parks and wildlife refuges.

◆ Landowners may harass, in a non-injurious manner, wolves on their land at any time.

◆ Landowners may kill a wolf caught in the act of killing or wounding livestock on their land. The incident must be reported to authorities within twenty-four hours and there must be evidence that livestock was attacked.

◆ The USFWS or authorized agencies may take (i.e., kill) wolves that are determined to be problem wolves. Problem wolves are those that in a calendar year attack livestock twice in a calendar year or attack domestic animals other than livestock.

◆ Land-use restrictions can only be enacted on public lands and only around acclimation pens and within 1 mile of active dens during spring. When six or more packs are present in the recovery area, closures around dens can only be enacted in national parks and wildlife refuges.

◆ Reintroduced wolves will be monitored via radio telemetry throughout the project. Any animal that is in need of special attention may be captured, treated if necessary, and re-released.

◆ Any person may take (i.e., kill) a gray wolf provided that the take is incidental to an otherwise lawful activity, accidental, unavoidable, unintentional, is not the result of negligent conduct lacking reasonable due care, and if due care was exercised to avoid taking the wolf. Such taking must be reported within twenty-four hours.

◆ Agencies may take any wolf that threatens humans, and anyone may kill a wolf in self-defense or in the defense of another person.

◆ All incidents involving wolves will be investigated by the USFWS. If the rules have been violated, penalties involving large fines and prison time may be levied.

In addition to these regulations, the Yellowstone reintroduction plan was supported by the Defenders of Wildlife, a nonprofit organization dedicated to helping recover wolves in their native habitats. The Defenders of Wildlife established a large mitigation fund from which ranchers and landowners could be compensated for the loss of any livestock killed by wolves on private or public grazing lands.

The idea of an experimental population is to get the wolves back into the ecosystem even if it means they don't have absolute protection from incidental kills and developments. The USFWS plan worked smoothly; wolves were brought in and they quickly formed mating pairs and established territories. A few wolves were killed, some illegally by folks who continue to despise the animals, but for the most part, the wolves flourished. If they are just left alone, it seems, the wolves will do well and don't need a lot of extra special attention.

Despite that, the Experimental Population tag almost killed the whole program, along with the reintroduced wolves. While all the paperwork was being processed, and the decisions being made in the early 1990s, a few Canadian wolves decided to take matters into their own paws. A handful of individuals and mated pairs drifted south along the eastern front of the Rocky Mountains, slowly moving into the Yellowstone Ecosystem and possibly even into central Idaho. Everyone knew these wolves were present, but their numbers were so tiny that there was no way they represented a viable, long-term population. But they were native, wild wolves and therefore were entitled to the full protections of the Endangered Species Act.

Wolf opponents seized on this fact and filed a lawsuit alleging that the Experimental Population was jeopardizing the natural population, on the grounds that once the experimental wolves were released, there would be no way to distinguish the native wolves from the reintroduced wolves. The judge on the case, U.S. District Court Judge William Downes, heard the arguments from the plaintiffs, led by the American Farm Bureau Federation, and agreed that the experimental wolves released violated a key section of the Endangered Species Act. That is, an experimental population is supposed to be kept "geographically separate" from existing wolf populations. The biologists with the USFWS acknowledged that individual wolves had occasionally wandered into the experimental zone in central Idaho, and possibly into Yellowstone, but they argued that these individuals didn't constitute a "population" because they neither reproduced nor stayed in the area. Judge Downes rejected that argument, ruling instead that the presence of even a single wolf, even a migratory wolf, constituted a population and therefore rendered the experimental population of reintroduced wolves in Idaho and in Yellowstone illegal.

The new populations had to be removed, Judge Downes ruled in December 1997. Not only the wolves that had been reintroduced, but all their offspring, as well. That, in essence, meant the wolves had to be killed, most likely by trapping or aerial shooting, because no state or province was interested in receiving the animals. But before any further action could be taken, he suspended his ruling while the Defenders of Wildlife and a coalition of wolf supporters appealed the decision.

The issue languished before the appellate court for nearly two years. Then, in January 2000, the Tenth U.S. Circuit Court of Appeals issued its decision: The wolves could stay. The Appellate Court, in overturning Judge Downes' decision, said the Endangered Species Act and the Experimental Population section added by Congress in 1982 were intended to allow the Interior Department flexibility in its approaches to the goals of preserving and aiding the recovery of threatened animals. The court ruling noted that a limit to that flexibility "ignores biological reality and misconstrues the larger purpose" of the law.

This ruling sets the stage for future reintroductions in wolf recovery zones along the Canadian border, the only areas where wild wolves might reinhabit the area on their own and so possibly create a conflict between native and reintroduced wolves. Now there is no legal reason not to proceed with wolf recovery efforts in the North Cascades Ecosystem. Of course, there are still plenty of political obstacles, and that has always been the problem. The obstacles are erected not only by wolf opponents but stem from the efforts of a few wolf supporters who hope to see the packs returned to Olympic National Park first.

Washington's Wolves

In the early 1990s there were numerous reports of wolves in North Cascades National Park, but despite the early excitement it now appears that these wolves were merely passing through. There is now no evidence of breeding pairs of wolves anywhere in Washington. But the fact that they have traveled through the state's lands suggests natural recovery is a possibility. Listening to the USFWS, you might guess that it is a sure thing, because: The USFWS Wolf Recovery Plan for the Northern Rockies, which includes wolf programs for Washington, relies solely on natural recovery for the return of the wolf population in the Cascades.

Mitch Friedman, Executive Director of the Northwest Ecosystem Alliance (NWEA), scoffs at this reliance. There are no wolves here, he asserts, and there aren't enough in the adjacent habitat in Canada to provide a viable, natural colonization effort. He says that if wolves are to return to the Cascades, we'll need to bring them back just as we did in Yellowstone and central Idaho, and as they are now doing with Mexican gray wolves in the southwestern United States. The problem, he says, is politics.

The best place to foster wolf recovery in Washington is within the North Cascades Ecosystem, Friedman says, but there is no political incentive to do that. The North Cascades doesn't have same the high-profile image of a premiere national park such as Yellowstone. But Olympic National Park certainly does. Therefore, one leading wolf-advocacy organization, the Defenders of Wildlife, has pushed for plans to return wolves to that park. Unfortunately, Olympic National Park is geographically isolated so there will never be any natural wolf recovery, and there is little habitat for the wolves beyond the borders of the sprawling park. That means any wolves that are returned to Olympic will exist as a genetically isolated population; there will be no cross-breeding with native populations, so no strengthening of the genetic stock. The other problem with the Olympic plan is a public one: The Olympic National Park is surrounded by human communities and settlements. Eventually, individual wolves, which have a natural propensity to roam, will stray from the park and the only place to go will be into human-inhabited areas. That will surely mean the death of those wolves. In the North Cascades, on the other hand, dispersing wolves can roam south along the wild lands of the Cascades all the way to California without being entangled with human settlements.

I would love to see wolves return in stable numbers to the Cascades, but because the political realities of today make that unlikely, I'm willing to go with the political flow and endorse the plans to reintroduce wolves to Olympic National Park. I firmly believe this plan has a good chance of coming to fruition within the next few years. Although the opponents of wolf recovery have been vocal in their opposition, they remain in the minority. A 1998 survey of the residents of Washington show that more than 62 percent of the populace supports reintroduction of gray wolves to Olympic National Park, and after the survey respondents were included in a brief discussion of the concerns and benefits of wolf reintroduction, the number jumped to 67 percent. And because the most vocal opposition of the plan has come from communities flanking the park, the researchers also analyzed how those communities would feel about wolf reintroduction. They found that, despite the fact that these communities would face the greatest impacts—both negative and positive—more than 51 percent initially favored the plans, and after a debate of the concerns and benefits, the support jumped to 56 percent in those local communities.

When asked why they support the plans to recover wolves in the park, the dominant answer was that they believed that wolves would enhance the quality of the Northwest and its wild lands. More than 76 percent said they believed that "although I may never see a wolf in the wild, it is important to me personally to know they exist in the Northwest." Interestingly, a similar percentage of the general public supports the belief that "although I may never visit a wilderness area, it is important to me to know these wild areas are protected." In contrast, opponents were unable to identify why they opposed wolf recovery. Responses ranged from "increased danger to hikers" and "loss of access to wild lands" to "a waste of tax payer dollars" and "why try to undo what we spent centuries doing (i.e., eradicating wolves)."

The public, obviously, supports wolf recovery in Washington. And Washingtonians like the fact that they may be returned to Olympic National Park because they are familiar with this hallmark park.

These things would be reason enough for a savvy politician to jump on board the "wolves in Olympic Park," bandwagon, but Representative Norm Dicks (D-Bremerton) has another reason to support the plans. Dicks, who certainly is one of the savviest and most powerful politicians in Congress, has thrown his support behind the Olympic wolf program on the advice of an old college friend, Roger Schlickeisen. These two attended the University of Washington together, and then went their separate ways—Dicks into public life, culminating in his tenured position in the U.S. House of Representatives, and Schlickeisen into public life by way of the nonprofit world. Schlickeisen is the president of Defenders of Wildlife, and when that organization decided to push for wolf recovery on the Olympic Peninsula of Washington, they called the most powerful congressman from that area—who happens to be one of the most powerful members of the entire House of Representatives and who also happens to be an old college chum of the Defenders of Wildlife president. So, given the public support and the chance to do a favor for an old friend, Dicks jumped on the program.

Through his political connections, Dicks was able to secure a $300,000 line item in the federal budget to fund a feasibility study of the wolf reintroduction idea. That is the first step toward recovery. If the study finds that wolves are indeed extinct in the park, and that there is adequate habitat and a prey base to support a population, the USFWS will be asked to progress with a full environmental assessment and publication of an EIS to chronicle the full extent of the impacts the wolf recovery would have on the Olympic Ecosystem and the surrounding communities. That process will take at least two years, and possibly as many as ten—though a likely timeline would be four or five years for the production of the final EIS once the feasibility study is completed. That means that wolves could be back in Olympic National Park by 2010, if not before.

Of course, there are still plenty of obstacles to this recovery. There are several agencies that need to be brought on board the wolf-recovery bandwagon, including the National Park Service, the U.S. Forest Service, the State Department of Fish and Wildlife, local governments, and Point No Point Treaty Council, a coalition of several Indian tribes on the Peninsula. So far, the greatest concerns have been expressed by the tribes.

It seems the elk herds around the Peninsula are suffering through a serious population decline, and the tribes rely on these herds for sustenance as well as for cultural and spiritual ceremonies. The Skokomish People, who are part of the Point No Point Treaty Council, hold the elk in a special place of honor among the wildlife they cherish. All wild animals are important to these people, but elk have a particular cultural significance, because they have historically relied so heavily on their meat for survival. The tribes maintain a connection with the elk through a special Elk ceremony that honors the first elk taken each season in order to show their respect and thanks to the animals.

During the 1998 International Wolf Conference hosted by the Defenders of Wildlife in Seattle, Sally Nickelson, spokesperson for the Point No Point Treaty Council, noted that the native people of the peninsula also revered wolves, but they were not considered essential to the cultural identity of the four tribes. That being the case, the tribes are very concerned about the status of the Peninsula's elk herds. The elk have already suffered a decline, and the tribal leaders fear that the introduction of wolves to the peninsula will hasten that decline, and possibly push the elk to the brink of extinction. That would have a devastating effect on the native people of the area, because they would lose a central element of their culture.

I can empathize with their concerns. I have no cultural connection with the elk, but as a true lover of wilderness and wildlife, I feel strongly about the need to have complete ecosystems—ecosystems where all the native species are represented with stable populations. I'm especially concerned about the Peninsula elk populations, because these are a subspecies of elk that doesn't exist anywhere else in the world. The Roosevelt Elk of the Olympics, named in honor of Theodore Roosevelt, who was the champion of establishing the park, are an integral part of the Peninsula's ecosystem. Fortunately, after seeing what has occurred in the Yellowstone Ecosystem, I am happily convinced that the tribes' concerns, though understandable, are largely unfounded. I see no evidence that the elk herds will suffer due to wolf reintroduction. Quite the opposite, in fact. I believe the herds could be revitalized and their populations stabilized or even increased by reintroducing their natural predator.

If we look at Yellowstone we see why this is so. There were similar concerns about potential impact of reintroduced wolves on the elk population of the Greater Yellowstone Ecosystem. In this case it wasn't Native Americans who were concerned, but big game hunters, especially commercial hunting guides. They were so adamant in their belief that the wolves would destroy the elk, and therefore their hunting and business opportunities, that they formed a new organization to oppose the wolf recovery.

The Friends of the Northern Yellowstone Elk Herd have claimed the wolves released into Yellowstone National Park in 1996 are responsible for a decline in the elk herds to the north of the park. The Northern Yellowstone elk herd includes more than 11,000 elk, which occupy a vast range that straddles the northern boundary of the park. The "Friends" say that the elk calf-to-cow ratio is down in recent years, that there are fewer calves with the female elk in the herd. But while this may be true, even though there is little substantive evidence to support the allegation, this ratio has little relationship to the size of the elk herd. Indeed, the Montana Department of Fish, Wildlife, and Parks reports that the elk herd has been stable throughout 1998 and 1999—at around 11,700 elk. Meanwhile, as the wolf pack inside Yellowstone National Park's boundary has grown from the 31 reintroduced in 1996 to more than 120 today, the Park's elk population has also grown, by as much as 10 percent! Because the wolves have largely stayed within the park boundaries—only a few stray outside the park to temporarily roam the adjacent lands—it would seem the wolves are not the reason for lack of growth among the elk outside the park.

A word about the dispersers is needed here. Though the majority of the reintroduced wolves and their offspring have been content to remain in the habitats where they were released, some individuals do succumb to the temptation to roam. The Idaho wolves—thirty-five were released in 1996—have multiplied enough that there are now eleven active, reproducing packs through the Idaho wildernesses, and some individuals are moving outside the area to find fresh territories. One wolf was found in 1999 on the Oregon side of Hells Canyon. In time, these dispersers could colonize the remote hills of the Wallowa Mountains and Blue Mountains of northeastern Oregon and southeastern Washington. These colonies, though, would be few and far between, and it is highly unlikely that there will be anything more than a few transient individuals in these areas for many years to come.

But back to the issue at hand: elk. These dispersers aren't going to have much impact on elk, because individual wolves are hard pressed to bring down an elk. They need the combined strength and strategy of the pack to tackle game this big.

As for the Northern Yellowstone elk herd, the park's wolves don't seem to be the deciding factor in the herd size—unless it's as a means to stimulate population growth among the elk. Bear in mind that hunting has never been allowed inside the park, so until the wolves were returned, the Park's elk had little predator control. Yet, inside the park, the elk herd has been stable over the years, and now that wolves are back, the population has grown. At the same time, elk hunting is a popular pastime outside the park. Beyond the Park's boundaries, the elk population has been stable or declining. Wolves clearly aren't responsible. But what about human hunters? Could they be the reason the non-park elk herd is not increasing in size and, in some local areas, is declining? Possibly. Not only do the locals enjoy hunting elk, but thousands of hunters from around the globe descend on western Montana in the fall to hunt the famous Rocky Mountain wapiti. These hunters from outside the area are the real motivation for the "Friends." The organization welcomes all hunters as members, but most of the money to keep the group going comes from commercial guides and outfitters. These hunting guides can pull in $3,000 per week to lead hunters into mountain camps and provide a chance to shoot an elk. But if the hunters go home without a trophy, it is unlikely they will return. To ensure that every hunter gets an elk, the guides need to have an abnormally high density of elk available.

The Yellowstone situation looks much like the one in the Olympic Peninsula. Both areas feature large elk herds split between National Park Service lands, where hunting is prohibited, and Forest Service lands, where hunting is allowed. Just as in Yellowstone, wolves were to be introduced into Olympic National Park and would, for the most part, stay there because that's where the vast majority of both habitat and prey are located.

But in both cases, local hunting interests—in Montana, guides and out-fitters, and in Washington, Indian tribes—fear that their opportunities to hunt elk on the adjoining Forest Service lands will disappear with the return of the wolves to the Park Service lands. Washingtonians can learn a lot in the next few years simply by watching the experiment in Yellowstone unfold. My feeling is that we will all be pleasantly surprised by how strong the entire ecosystem will become now that nearly all the original species are repre-sented once again. The interaction of predators and prey improves the health and long-term viability of both species, and that can only be good for all of us two-legged wilderness lovers.

The History of Wolves on the Olympic Peninsula

Before we look too far into the future, it's worth taking a moment to look to the past. By understanding our history with wolves perhaps we can look forward to a more harmonious future. The story of humans and wolves in Washington is the same as the story elsewhere: We came in and killed the beasts as quickly, and with as little effort, as we possibly could.

The decline of the wolf population on the Peninsula really began during the winter of 1805-06 when the Corps of Discovery, led by Captains Meriwether Lewis and William Clark, established Fort Clatsop on the south side of the Columbia River, near present-day Astoria, Washington. They spent the long winter in this fort before returning to the east the following spring. During their stay in Clatsop, Lewis wrote in his journal about the local wolves, describing them as large, brown specimens. After Lewis and Clark returned to the states, there was a long period of years when few, if any, Americans ventured back out into the wilds of the Oregon Territory. But the British quickly moved into the region, by way of Canada. They established Fort Vancouver, near present-day Vancouver, Washington, and Fort Nisqually, near what is now Olympia. In 1821, Fort Nisqually received 250 wolf pelts from trappers. This is the first record of wolves being killed in number on the Peninsula.

In 1854, the new Washington Territory passed a territorial law establish-ing a bounty for predators. The bounties varied from county to county, but they ranged from $1 per hide in Jefferson County to $5 per hide in Clallam County. Over the next 50 years, the bounties changed repeatedly. Sometimes they were paid by the territorial government, sometimes by the counties. The predator bounties were a huge draw on the already slim public budgets, yet the practice continued. At times, bounty hunters would collect multiple bounties for each animal; fraud was common and easy to perpetrate. According to some records, predator bounty hunters could collect up to $50 per pelt—this at a time when the average wage was on the order of $30 per month. One individual is said to have collected bounty on as many as 800 cougars. In today's dollars, the bounty on those cats would have earned the savvy hunter about $500,000.

By the beginning of the twentieth century, the counties had largely abolished their predator bounties, but the state continued to pay for the killing of wolves. In 1920, the last documented wild wolf on the Olympic Peninsula was killed in the upper Elwha Valley—within the National Park boundaries!

The wolves haven't howled in the deep rainforests, or high Olympic Peaks, since then. But the reintroduction efforts launched in 1998 could very well mean they will howl there again within the next decade.

Debunking Wolf Myths

Humans have developed a lot of stories about wolves, many of which have been shaped through generations of telling and retelling. Eventually, what were once fact-based concerns became exaggerated tall tales and myths. Many of the myths and legends had their origins in Europe and Asia, where wolves and humans have interacted for many millennia. When these myths were applied to North American wolves, they fell even further from reality.

I took a look at some of the more common, and most prevalent, myths concerning wolves and wolf recovery, and found that the facts paint quite a different picture. Here are some of them.

Myth: Wolves are evil beasts that will ruthlessly attack humans.

Facts: Wolf biologists throughout North America have different ideas and perspectives on wolves, but there is one point on which all seem to be in complete agreement: There is no documented case in North America of a healthy wolf seriously injuring, let alone killing, a human. Note the inclusion of the word healthy. Rabid wolves may indeed have attacked humans in years past, but any rabid animal, be it a mouse, raccoon, or your favorite house pet, is likely to attack. Wolves, by nature, are shy and generally go to a lot of trouble to avoid humans. Of course, as more wolves return to the wilds of the Lower 48 and more humans head out into those same wilds to recreate, there is a chance there will be encounters. No biologist will outright guarantee your safety when talking about a wild animal. But the fact remains that there has never been a death caused by a healthy wolf, and there is only one documented incident in the United States in the last 120 years of a wolf threatening a person. In that case, the wolf had been separated from its pack and was scared and alone. By contrast, since 1980, more than 300 people have been killed in the United States by domestic dogs.

Myth: Wolves will slaughter domestic sheep and cattle that graze on public and private lands in or near the recovery areas.

Facts: Wolf recovery in these areas may actually reduce the loss of livestock, because wolves seem to always prefer to hunt wild ungulates (deer, elk, moose, etc.) over domestic stock when given a choice. Coyotes, on the other hand, will often slip into a ranch and kill newborn calves and lambs whenever they can. Because wolves hate coyotes, and kill them on sight, the reintroduction of wolves means a rapid and substantial reduction in the local coyote population, thereby reducing the predation of domestic livestock. In Minnesota, which, with more than 2,200 wolves has the largest population in the Lower 48, fewer than one-tenth of one percent of the deaths of livestock herds have been attributed to wolves. Hardly a slaughter.

Moreover, should a wolf attack livestock, the nonprofit organization Defenders of Wildlife has established a compensation fund that pays for the loss of any stock animal killed by reintroduced wolves.

Myth: Wolves will decimate the big game populations, especially of deer and elk.

Facts: This is the silliest of the myths. Wolves evolved alongside their prey base, and all species have thrived in the tens of thousands of years they have existed together in North America. Aldo Leopold noted that the wolf has shaped the deer and elk into the beautiful creations they are today, and have controlled their populations effectively so that the browsers didn't overgraze any ecosystem. In short, the wolves keep the deer and elk population in balance with the land.

Some argue that that works fine in a natural system, but our current system has been corrupted by human involvement. Wolves, they say, aren't the only hunters anymore. Humans also hunt these species, and the combined pressures of wolves and human hunters on the prey species would be too much for them. This argument certainly has merit, and there may be a need to revise hunting seasons in some areas, but recent studies indicate that wolf predation may actually foster stronger, more stable populations of prey species. More research has to be done, but one thing is quite clear—wolves will not decimate any prey populations. They have caused a short-term reduction in herd size, but that causes an immediate change in the wolf pack. When food gets scarce, the pack's breeding female knows, at a genetic level, that there isn't enough food to support a lot of pups. So her body either skips a season of breeding or, if she does breed, she produces a very small litter. In other words, when the prey base declines, the predator population declines, too.

Myth: Wolf recovery is extremely expensive.

Fact: The initial cost seems steep: several million dollars to capture, acclimate, release and monitor a few dozen wolves. But once the wolves are in place, the costs diminish greatly, largely because the wolves have proven so willing and able to stay and breed in the areas. It is also estimated that the return of wolves to the Yellowstone Ecosystem may help to boost the local tourism business—from the sale of wolf memorabilia to increased hotel bookings—by as much as 10 percent. Wolves have become the darling of the general public, and just having them in the area will draw tourists who might otherwise go elsewhere.

Myth: Wolf recovery will shut down the remaining logging activities, which could destroy the already-struggling communities near the recovery areas.

Facts: With the reintroduction of an "experimental population," the restrictions on such activities as logging and mining are negligible. The only strict curbs on developments are within a mile of the denning sites when cubs are present. Because that is a very small area, there is virtually no impact on land use. Also wolf recovery in Washington will be focused on Olympic National Park, and it is unlikely that wolves will stray outside the park for more than a brief foray. There is little suitable wolf habitat beyond the park borders and in the North Cascades, especially within the North Cascades National Park Complex. Land uses such as logging and mining are already off limits in these areas.

Myth: Trails will be closed if wolves return to the backcountry.

Fact: See the above statement. The only restrictions will be on development within a mile of breeding dens, and even then, trails won't be closed. There might be temporary restrictions on camping near denning sights, if those dens are close to established camping areas, but even this is unlikely because wolves prefer to make the dens in remote, quiet areas well away from humans.

Meeting Wolves in the Woods

Today there is virtually no chance you'll encounter wolves while hiking or backpacking. But it may be that just a few years down the road we will be sharing the backcountry with *Canis lupus*. When that time comes, you'll need to be aware of the proper techniques and precautions to take to ensure the safety of yourself and the wolves.

When traveling in wolf habitat, always "bear bag" your food and scented clothing to avoid attracting predators of any kind. Today, anywhere you are in wolf country, you are also in cougar country, black bear country and probably grizzly bear country.

If you see a wolf or wolves, there are a couple things you should do. First and foremost, consider yourself very lucky. Few people are privileged enough to see wild wolves. Second, stay calm and quiet. You have little or nothing to fear. There has never been a documented case of a healthy wolf attacking an adult human in North America. If you stay quiet, you might be able to view the wolf or wolves for a while before they become aware of you and flee.

Finally, when you get back to town, call the Washington Department of Wildlife or the USFWS and report the sighting. Signs are being set up at trailheads encouraging people to report wolf sightings. Should anyone see a wolf, hear wolves howling, or find their tracks, they can report it to the nearest available agency office or call the wolf sighting hotline, listed in Appendix B.

Encountering a wolf in the wild is an experience I would cherish as a special blessing. There is no reason to fear the great hunters, and a host of reasons why we should look forward to such sightings. Not only are the animals truly beautiful and majestic, they are an integral part of the spirit of the wilderness. In fact, as much as I long to see wolves roaming the wilds of Washington, I'm more excited about the possibility of hearing them. The soaring notes of the wolf song are the anthem of the American wilderness, and it's been far too long since that song has been played in this state.

Chapter 7

The Interaction of Species
and the Future of Predators

In the 200-year history of this nation, we have showcased our ability to decimate species. Sometimes we have done it unintentionally, out of sheer ignorance. This was the case with the passenger pigeon and the bison. Hunters simply blasted away at the seemingly endless flocks of pigeons and the miles-long herds of bison until eventually there were no more.

Sometimes we have done it out of fear or simple spite. This has been the case with our nation's predators. In an attempt to "civilize" the wilderness and make it safe for us, our families, and our domesticated animals, we worked tirelessly to eliminate the wild animals that frightened us, threatened our livestock, or simply weren't desirable as game animals. We have shot, trapped, and poisoned every wolf, coyote, cougar, bear, bobcat, lynx, wolverine, and badger we encountered from the time the first Europeans set foot on the North American continent right up to present day. That's right. Predator extermination is an ongoing process. Just ask the coyotes, 90,000 of which are killed by government-funded "hunters" each year.

The killing is slowly giving way to sympathy and an understanding of the role of predators in the natural systems of this continent. We have removed all the grizzlies and wolves, driven the lynx into the most remote corners of our northlands, and wiped out the wolverines nationwide. As a result, deer and elk populations are alternately booming and busting, because the natural population regulators are gone. We see lesser predators like the coyote surging in numbers, taking over the former ranges of the more dominant predators that we've removed. But these new predators don't behave the same as their predecessors. Instead of solely hunting deer and elk like the wolves, coyotes instead tear into sheep and calves. Cougars, instead of steering clear of humans and their pets, may now stalk human children—who look more like prey than adult humans—and snatch pets off back porches. And they take down more mature deer than the wolves they have replaced.

We are learning now that the best way to control these "problem predator populations" is to restore the other predators. Over the eons, nature has developed a fine balance in which all species can survive and thrive together, but only if each is present to fulfill its role in the ecosystem.

The Interaction of Predator Species

There's an interesting dynamic at work when we see more and more species of predators returning to an ecosystem. Although the number of species increases, the pressure on the local prey populations typically stays much the same. That's because secondary predators are displaced or killed by primary predators. For instance, coyotes and cougars are bumped out when grizzlies and wolves return.

They don't disappear entirely, but their numbers are reduced to a more natural figure. This happens in a number of ways. In the case of cougars, they may be killed outright by wolves or grizzly bears—especially if they venture too near a wolf den or a grizzly sow with cubs. They may be driven away from the territory they had been occupying and then killed by other cougars when they enter an already occupied cougar territory. Or they could starve.

As unlikely as this last method of natural cougar population reduction sounds, it seems to happen far more often than the other method. When cougars are the primary predator—as they are throughout Washington State as this book is going to press—they can enjoy every kill they make. That is, they can kill a deer and consume it over a period of a week or more, which is a normal amount of time to finish off a kill. This means that cougars only have to hunt about one out of seven days.

Add wolves and grizzly bears to the cougar's habitat, though, and that changes. Studies done by the Hornocker Institute in Yellowstone National Park and the Flathead Valley of northwestern Montana show that cougars in multi-predator ecosystems are displaced off their kills as often as 60 percent of the time. A cougar will bring down a deer or elk, feed on it immediately, then stash the carcass somewhere—usually burying it in leaves and forest debris—to feed on later. Before the cougar can enjoy more than a couple meals, though, the carcass is discovered and claimed by wolves or bears. Even coyotes have been known to displace cougars. The result is the cougar has less food from each kill, so instead of hunting once every week, it may need to make a kill twice or even three times each week. That is easier said than done. The cats expend a lot of energy in each pursuit, and if they aren't fully fed and rested before they have to hunt again, their odds of success drop.

Add in the fact that each time the cougar hunts, it puts itself at considerable risk—remember, more than a third of cougar deaths occur when they are pursuing their prey—and we get a clearer view of just how other predator species can control cougar population numbers. Simply by taking their food, they weaken the cats and force them into hazard situations more often.

But cougars are the ultimate hunters. They can take down and kill elk, which are five or six times their size. Why would they flee from coyotes and wolves? Numbers. Cougars are solitary beasts, while the canines are pack animals. A pack of coyotes or wolves can surround and harass a cougar until it gives up and flees. As for bears, cougars have a relatively small body mass compared to American black bears and grizzlies so they seldom put up much argument when a bear decides it wants the cougar's food stash.

As the cougars learn to live with other predators, they actually voluntarily leave an area, or at least decide not to attempt to reenter an area once the local cougar population has been reduced. The cougars of Yellowstone Ecosystem appear to have learned to restrict themselves to habitats in which there is less likelihood of conflict with the more dominant predators.

Much the same thing happens to coyotes when wolves return to an ecosystem. In Yellowstone, the coyote population had risen from nothing in the early part of the twentieth century to being the dominant predator in the 1990s. But in the four years that wolves have been back in the park, the coyote population has been slashed by half. Wolves will not tolerate coyotes in their territory. If they see them, they will kill them or pursue them until the coyotes flee the wolves' range. They also displace the coyotes from their kills, thus starving them out of the area, just as they do with cougars.

But not all the coyotes, or the cougars, will disappear from the ecosystems. Rather, their populations will be reduced to a number that fits within the balance of the system. This means there will be a population that is viable and self-sustaining but which doesn't stress the prey base beyond its abilities to support all the predator species.

Once this balance is achieved, it appears that the various predator species actually benefit from each other's presence. For instance, scavengers, including wolves, black bears, grizzlies, coyotes, bobcats, and birds, visited 60 percent of cougar kills in Yellowstone. Likewise, the new Yellowstone wolves are creating buffets for the other meat-eaters of the park. Wolf packs are incredibly efficient hunting units, and they bring down a lot of deer and elk. That puts a lot of meat on the ground all year long. The wolves will immediately start eating their prey, and they'll continue gorging themselves until they can barely walk. The wolves will each consume as much as 20 pounds of fresh meat and guts from their freshly killed elk, a deer or a bison. But even a large pack can't eat an entire elk in one sitting. Instead, each member of the pack will stuff themselves until they can't swallow another bite, then stagger off to a quiet, sheltered area where they'll pass out—falling into what some wolf biologists have called a "meat stupor." They'll sleep soundly while their bodies process and digest the giant meal.

Back at the kill, however, as much as half of the meat is left on the ground, open for any scavenger to come in and steal a free meal. And plenty are doing just that. With all the wolf kills in the park these days, grizzly bears and bald eagles are benefiting, but so are some individual coyotes, foxes, ravens, magpies, bears, and golden eagles, as well as a host of smaller birds and mammals.

The park's grizzly bears seem to be the biggest winners in the wolves' return—aside from the wolves themselves, that is. For years, grizzlies rarely ventured into the Lamar Valley in the fall, but since wolves were released there in 1995 the great bears have become a common sight in the broad valley come autumn. The bears, in fact, sometimes seem to work together with the wolves. Occasionally, of course, the big grizzlies simply drive wolves away from the kills, stealing their meat. But park biologists have also observed the two species traveling together, and sometimes even killing together.

Grizzly bear biologist Steve French told the Bozeman *Chronicle* that biologists have witnessed an individual grizzly bear walk up to a carcass with nine wolves on it and scare them off. But, he added, they've also witnessed more cooperative encounters. For instance, during the autumn of 1998, biologists observed a grizzly sow with two cubs traveling with a couple of wolves for about a week. The unlikely groups located game together and actually shared the kill—eating side by side.

On the other hand, individual wolves have been seen following grizzlies to prey carcasses, then feeding on that meat when the bear wanders off. It's a two-way street, it seems, but the most common scenario is the other way around, with the bear sharing or stealing a wolf kill. This doesn't seem to be adversely affecting the wolves, and it certainly is helping the bears. Not only are the bears adding more meat to their diets, which generally consist of 90 to 95 percent plant matter, but they suddenly have a food source available longer into the fall. That means they can delay entering hibernation dens, which in turn means they emerge in the spring with more fat reserves and in better overall condition.

There may still be some folks who don't appreciate the wolves' return to the wilds of Montana and Idaho, but the local bears certainly aren't among them.

The Necessity of Predators

All this interaction—be it conflict or cooperation—helps illustrate that predators are a fundamental, indeed a vital part of our natural ecosystems. Wherever there are predators, ecosystems grow and thrive, producing amazing numbers and varieties of species. Wherever predators disappear, ecosystems become stale and stagnant, with a few exceptionally successful species crowding out all others and taking over the entire habitat. The role of predators isn't merely to cull the herds of their prey animals, but to keep those animals strong and viable as a species. Most animal species have evolved in environments that include predators and other natural enemies, and to maintain their genetic strengths—whether it's the fleet-footedness of antelope or the alertness and nimbleness of blacktail deer—these species need those predators around them. The predators also keep prey from over-exploiting their environment. Throughout the world, nearly every species—especially prey species—produces more offspring than the available resources can support. If all those offspring survived, the result would be disastrous. They would rapidly eat all the available food, and then the entire species would starve. Fortunately, that rarely if ever happens in natural systems due to the pressures exerted on the prey populations by predators. Wolves, cougars, and coyotes will cull excess offspring and weak or inferior (i.e., slow or injured) individuals from the prey population, thus helping keep the prey's numbers under control.

So what happens if we remove the predators? Are the prey animals going to suddenly stop producing a surplus of young? Nope. The animals keep breeding as fast as ever, expanding as long as there's enough food to support them. In North America, the deer and elk herds have grown substantially since the end of the nineteenth century, but they haven't become overwhelming largely because of human hunting pressures. Still, deer are a problem in some areas of America. Their populations have exceeded the natural habitat's carrying capacity and have moved into agricultural lands for food. In Washington's Blue Mountains, many farmers complain of elk herds in the wheat fields, and orchardists in the Naches and Yakima Valleys have been found illegally shooting elk that have started munching on their apple trees.

I've seen this type of population bloom happen in the area around Lyons Ferry State Park along the Snake River in southeastern Washington. The area around the park, and its adjacent fish hatchery, was cleared of rattlesnakes. Workers from the hatchery and the park would kill any snake on sight, and when they had a free moment, they'd hunt out snakes to kill. Eventually, the snake population was reduced to nearly nothing. The workers were happy—they felt safe sending their kids out to play in the yard, even though they never had a problem with the kids being bitten by snakes before.

But soon problems developed. With no snakes, the local mouse population exploded. Soon mice were chewing through the houses of the hatchery workers, building nests in the engines of their cars, and generally wreaking havoc throughout the area. Poisons were laid out, traps were set, and suddenly pets and children were endangered once more—this time by the presence of the traps and poison the people had used in place of the snakes. Snakes have been allowed to return to the area—they aren't killed on sight anymore unless they are in the yards of the homes in the area, or otherwise in direct contact with the inhabited areas—and the mice population is diminishing.

In Montana, the problems of overpopulation of prey species take a different form. There, rather than losing farm profits to deer and elk, or seeing damage done by the booming population of pests, they are seeing an increase in the spread of disease from the large herds of wildlife (elk and bison) to their domestic herds.

The answer to all these problems could be—probably is—as simple as returning natural predators into the equation. Human hunters don't control prey populations, they merely knock the edge of the population spikes each fall. Wolves hunt year round, and they take the animals that should be culled (the injured, weak, and genetically inferior) to keep the herds strong. Humans, on the other hand, tend to take the healthiest, most genetically superior animals (everyone wants the big set of antlers for the wall). When predators are returned to the system, they almost immediately bring the prey animal's population under control again. We see that happening in Yellowstone, in Idaho, and we're beginning to see it in New Mexico and Arizona where the Mexican wolf has been reintroduced.

We are starting to see that predators are actually more beneficial than we ever thought, and that has helped smooth the processes of recovery and reintroduction.

Predator-friendly Products: The Wave of the Future?

More and more, the American public makes its buying decisions with an eye toward the environment. We have organic and chemical-free produce, dolphin-safe tuna, hormone-free milk, and free-range chickens. And now some ranchers have banded together to market the latest environmentally friendly farm product: predator-friendly wool and beef. The movement got its start in Montana and Idaho, where the Growers' Wool Cooperative launched a Predator-Friendly Wool Certification program. The certificate

program provides ranchers incentives to seek coexistence with native predators in the hopes that they will find that more beneficial than working toward their destruction. To receive the certificate for the wool, ranchers must
protect their sheep from predators—including coyotes, cougars, bears and
wolves—using non-lethal methods. Some of the approved options for protection are enclosing pastures in predator-proof fencing (an electric fence
works well) and utilizing guard animals other than just dogs. The inclusion
of a few llamas or burros in a herd of sheep proves an effective deterrent to
most predators. These animals are more alert than domestic sheep and are
far more willing to challenge a coyote, cougar, or bear than the docile sheep
in the herd. And more predators will back down when their prey turns and
challenges them—after all, there's easier prey than that which fights.

The sheep ranchers who earn the Predator-Friendly Wool label have
found that their product—even if it is of similar quality with their neighbors—will sell for much higher price. The eco-label earns them a premium
price, and the kicker is that predator-friendly practices are as cost-effective
as the other, more lethal options such as trapping or shooting.

A similar program has been launched in Arizona and New Mexico, where
cattle ranchers have teamed up with the local chapters of the Defenders of
Wildlife to create an eco-label for beef: Wolf County Beef. To earn the right to
label their beef as wolf-friendly, the ranchers agree to support the efforts of
the U.S. Fish and Wildlife Service (USFWS) to reintroduce Mexican wolves
into the wilds of the American Southwest, even if it means the wolves may
be released on public lands for which they own the grazing rights. That is,
the ranchers agree to support the wolf program even when the wolves may
be neighbors to their cows. In return, Defenders of Wildlife promises to pay
for any livestock losses due to predation. The program has the support of a
broad coalition of ranchers, with more than 70,000 acres of ranch and grazing land included in the program as of early 2000.

Whenever innovative programs like these are introduced, they face a
few tall hurdles. There are always skeptics who don't believe it will work, or
that the labels are merely marketing ploys that have no basis in fact—as has
been the case with some dolphin-safe tuna packaging. But even if that is
case—and I don't believe it is here—the idea that there's a market for the
predator-safe idea is heartening. It shows that the American people have
developed an appreciation for predators and are willing to support them
with their wallets. I believe that the predator-friendly labels on ranch products, whether wool, beef, lamb chops or leather, will prove to be more than a

marketing gimmick. Organic produce has moved from a small niche in the food production industry into a mainstream concept—while once you had to search food co-ops or farmer's markets to get organic products, now most large grocery stores have organic sections in their produce departments. I believe the same will be true with predator-friendly products. The general public is growing more savvy when it comes to shopping, and the more they learn about farm and ranch practices, the more they are demanding changes to the old ways of doing things. We don't want so many chemicals on our food, we don't want growth hormones injected in cows to make our milk more nutritious, and we don't want ranchers poisoning coyotes in order to keep our wool clothing cheap.

The Future of Predators

The American public often expresses strong support for wildlife of all kind, and there has been a population shift from urban and suburban areas into more rural settings. More and more people are moving to the country "to be closer to nature." Yet they are finding that nature isn't as benevolent as Walt Disney would have us believe. Bears don't wander around as companions to friendly mountain folks, deer aren't cuddly, harmless animals, and certainly the natural world isn't as safe and serene as we might think. Life in nature is a violent existence. Something has to die for others to live. Killing is a routine occurrence in nature. It's not a matter of good and evil, but a matter of life and death.

Country dwellers that make up this new generation find that they are having to change their perceptions. They want to live close to nature but have all too often been shocked and even outraged when they find nature on their back porch. Coyotes snatch up their cats, cougars eat their dogs, deer devour their gardens, and raccoons ransack their garbage cans.

Some of these folks decide to try to civilize their new homes by having the authorities kill or transplant all the predators and wild animals that wander into their yards. But, I'm pleased to say, for every person that decides they want to civilize the wilderness in the backyard, there are another two or three that revel in their new-found connection with the natural world.

People are learning to live with nature—death, destruction, and all—and they want to ensure that their kids can have the same experience. The American public has shown a new-found appreciation for all wildlife. And for the most part, Americans endorse the idea of restoring our wildernesses to their full complement of species.

The process will be slow, and many battles remain to be fought, but during the new millennium, I'm sure we'll see more and more ecosystems made whole and complete with the reintroduction of predators. I'm glad I'll be here to see it happen.

Appendix A: Bibliography

General

Alden, Peter and Paulson, Dennis. *National Audubon Society Field Guide to the Pacific Northwest.* New York, N.Y.: Alfred A. Knopf, 1998.

Bass, Rick. *The Book of Yaak.* New York, N.Y.: Houghton Mifflin Co., 1996.

Childs, Craig. *Crossing Paths: Uncommon Encounters with Animals in the Wild.* Seattle, Wash.: Sasquatch Books, 1997.

Leopold, Aldo. *Round River: From the Journals of Aldo Leopold.* New York, N.Y.: Oxford University Press, 1993 (first published 1953).

Leopold, Aldo. *A Sand County Almanac, and Sketches Here and There.* New York, N.Y.: Oxford University Press, 1987 (first published 1949).

Mathews, Daniel. *Cascade-Olympic Natural History: A Trailside Reference.* Portland, Oreg.: Raven Editions. 1988.

Matthiessen, Peter. *Wildlife in America.* New York, N.Y.: Viking-Penguin Books, 1987.

Moulton, Gary E., ed. *The Journals of the Lewis and Clark Expedition.* Lincoln, Nebr.: University of Nebraska Press, 1986.

Nash, Roderick. *Wilderness and the American Mind.* New Haven, Conn.: Yale University Press, 1973 (first published 1967).

Savage, Arthur and Savage, Candace. *Wild Mammals of Northwest America.* Baltimore, Md.: Johns Hopkins Press, 1981.

Turbak, Gary. *Survivors in the Shadows: Threatened and Endangered Mammals of the American West.* Flagstaff, Ariz.: Northland Publishing Co., 1993.

Winnie, John Jr. *High Life: Animals of the Alpine World.* Flagstaff, Ariz.: Northland Publishing, 1996.

The Cat Family: Cougars, Lynx, and Bobcats

Bolgiano, Chris. *Mountain Lion: An Unnatural History of Pumas and People.* Mechanicsburg, Pa.: Stackpole Books, 1995.

Busch, Robert H. *The Cougar Almanac: A Complete Natural History of the Mountain Lion.* New York, N.Y.: Lyons and Burford, 1996.

Danz, Harold P. *Cougar!* Athens, Ohio: Ohio University Press, 1999.

Ewing, Susan and Grossman, Elizabeth, eds. *Shadow Cat: Encountering the American Mountain Lion.* Seattle, Wash.: Sasquatch Books, 1999.

Hanson, Kevin. *Cougar: the American Lion.* Flagstaff, Ariz.: Northland Publishing (In association with the Mountain Lion Foundation), 1992.

McCall, Karen and Dutcher, Jim. *Cougar: Ghost of the Rockies.* San Francisco, Calif.: Sierra Club Books, 1992.

Savage, Candace. *Wild Cats: Lynx, Bobcats and Mountain Lions.* San Francisco, Calif.: Sierra Club Books, 1993.

Seidensticker, John and Lumpkin, Susan, eds. *Great Cats: Majestic Creatures of the Wild.* Emmaus, Pa.: Rodale Press, 1991.

Torres, Steven. *Mountain Lion Alert: Safety Tips for Yourself, Your Children, Your Pets and Your Livestock in Cougar Country.* Helena, Mont.: Falcon Publishing, 1997.

The Canine Family: Wolves and Coyotes

Bass, Rick. *The New Wolves.* New York, N.Y.: The Lyons Press, 1998.

Bass, Rick. *The Ninemile Wolves.* Livingston, Mont.: Clark City Press, 1992.

Busch, Robert H. *The Wolf Almanac: A Celebration of Wolves and Their World.* New York, N.Y.: Lyons and Burford, 1995.

Fox, Michael W. *The Soul of the Wolf: A Meditation on Wolves and Man.* New York, N.Y.: Lyons and Burford, 1980.

Grooms, Steve. *The Return of the Wolf.* Minocqua, Minn.: Northword Press, Inc., 1993.

Jenkins, Ken L. *Wolf Reflections.* Merrillville, Ind.: ICS Books, 1996.

Lawrence, R.D. *Trail of the Wolf.* Emmaus, Pa.: Rodale Press, 1993.

Lopez, Barry. *Of Wolves and Men.* New York, N.Y.: Charles Scribner's Sons, 1978.

Mech, L. David. *The Way of the Wolf.* Stillwater, Minn.: Voyageur Press, 1991.

Mech, L. David. *The Wolf: The Ecology and Behavior of an Endangered Species.* Minneapolis, Minn.: University of Minnesota, 1992 (first printed, 1970).

Murray, John A., ed. *Out Among the Wolves: Contemporary Writings on the Wolf.* Seattle, Wash.: Alaska Northwest Books, 1993.

Turbak, Gary. *Twilight Hunters: Wolves, Coyotes and Foxes.* Flagstaff, Ariz.: Northland Publishing, 1992 (first printed, 1987).

Wilkinson, Todd. *Track of the Coyote.* Minocqua, Wis.: Northwood Press, 1995.

Wolfe, Art. *In the Presence of Wolves.* New York, N.Y.: Crown Publishing, 1995.

Bruins: Grizzly Bears and American Black Bears

Bass, Rick. *The Lost Grizzlies: A Search for Survivors in the Wilderness of Colorado.* New York, N.Y.: Houghton Mifflin Co., 1995.

Brown, Gary. *The Great Bear Almanac.* New York, N.Y.: Lyons and Burford, 1993.

Dufresne, Frank. *No Room for Bears.* Seattle, Wash.: Alaska Northwest Books, 1991.

Jenkins, Ken. *Black Bear Reflections.* Merrillville, Ind.: ICS Books, 1995.

Lynch, Wayne. *Bears: Monarchs of the Northern Wilderness.* Seattle, Wash.: The Mountaineers Books, 1993.

McMillion, Scott. *Mark of the Grizzly: True Stories of Recent Bear Attacks and the Hard Lessons Learned.* Helena, Mont.: Falcon Publishing, 1998.

Murray, John A., ed. *The Great Bear: Contemporary Writings on the Grizzly.* Seattle, Wash.: Alaska Northwest Books, 1992.

Peacock, Doug. *Grizzly Years: In Search of the American Wilderness.* New York, N.Y.: Henry Holt and Co., 1990.

Schneider, Bill. *Bear Aware: Hiking and Camping in Bear Country.* Helena, Mont.: Falcon Publishing, 1996.

Smith, Dave. *Backcountry Bear Basics: The Definitive Guide to Avoiding Unpleasant Encounters.* Seattle, Wash.: The Mountaineers Books, 1997.

Stirling, Ian, ed. *Bears: Majestic Creatures of the Wild.* Emmaus, Pa.: Rodale Press, 1993.

Walker, Tom and Aumiller, Larry. *River of Bears.* Stillwater, Minn.: Voyageur Press, Inc. 1993.

Appendix B: Additional Resources

Beyond the Bookshelf

For those who want to do more than read about predators and are within driving distance of Puget Sound, there is a wonderful opportunity to get a real feel for the wild animals. Northwest Trek Wildlife Park near Eatonville offers an up-close and personal look at grizzly bears, American black bears, cougars, lynx, bobcats, coyotes, wolves, and wolverines in natural settings.

The curators of the facility have brought in tens of thousands of native plants to create wildlife enclosures that are as natural as any fenced facilities can be. Situated on the 600-acre wildlife park, Northwest Trek is an educational resource for the public and a research facility for wildlife managers. In addition to the secure, natural-environment exhibits featuring the predators, there is a vast free-roam area that is home to most of the large prey species that are native to the United States, including deer, elk, bison, bighorn sheep, and mountain goats. The free-roam area can be viewed from the comfort of a tram ride that loops through the entire park past the free-roaming herds.

Northwest Trek is located just off Highway 161 between Puyallup and Eatonville and is administered by Tacoma's Point Defiance Zoo. For more information, call (206) 847-1901.

Web Sites

The Great Bear Foundation: *www.greatbear.org/*

The Hornocker Wildlife Institute: *www.uidaho.edu/rsrch/hwi/*

Northwest Ecosystem Alliance: *www.ecosystem.org/*

United States Fish and Wildlife Service (USFWS): *www.fws.gov/*

USFWS, Region 1 (Pacific Region): *www.pacific.fws.gov/*

Washington Department of Fish and Wildlife: *www.wa.gov/wdfw/*

Wolf Haven International: www.wolfhaven.org/

Telephone Numbers

Wolf sighting hotline: 1-800-722-4095

Insight Wildlife Management, Inc., and World Society for the Protection of Animals: 1-800-542-BEAR

International Wolf Center: 1-800-ELY-WOLF

U.S. Fish and Wildlife Service—Pacific Region: 1-503-231-6121

Washington Department of Fish and Wildlife: 1-360-902-2200

Index

About the Author

Dan A. Nelson is executive editor of *Signpost for Northwest Trails,* a monthly backcountry recreation magazine published by the Washington Trails Association (WTA). Other Mountaineers Books by Nelson are *Best of the Pacific Crest Trail: Washington* (2000), *Snowshoe Routes: Washington* (1998), and the WTA-authored *Accessible Trails in Washington's Backcountry: A Guide to 85 Outings* (1995), for which Nelson served as writer and editor. Nelson is also co-author of *Pacific Northwest Hiking: The Complete Guide to 1,000 of the Best Hikes in Washington and Oregon* (Foghorn Press, 1997) .

He is also an outdoor recreation feature writer and columnist for *The Seattle Times'* outdoors and travel sections, as well as a frequent contributor to *BACKPACKER* magazine. An avid hiker, backpacker, skier, and snowshoer, Nelson has explored and photographed wilderness areas throughout the West. He lives in Puyallup, Washington.

THE MOUNTAINEERS, founded in 1906, is a nonprofit outdoor activity and conservation club, whose mission is "to explore, study, preserve, and enjoy the natural beauty of the outdoors. . . . " Based in Seattle, Washington, the club is now the third-largest such organization in the United States, with 15,000 members and five branches throughout Washington State.

The Mountaineers sponsors both classes and year-round outdoor activities in the Pacific Northwest, which include hiking, mountain climbing, ski-touring, snowshoeing, bicycling, camping, kayaking and canoeing, nature study, sailing, and adventure travel. The club's conservation division supports environmental causes through educational activities, sponsoring legislation, and presenting informational programs. All club activities are led by skilled, experienced volunteers, who are dedicated to promoting safe and responsible enjoyment and preservation of the outdoors.

If you would like to participate in these organized outdoor activities or the club's programs, consider a membership in The Mountaineers. For information and an application, write or call The Mountaineers, Club Headquarters, 300 Third Avenue West, Seattle, WA 98119; 206-284-6310.

The Mountaineers Books, an active, nonprofit publishing program of the club, produces guidebooks, instructional texts, historical works, natural history guides, and works on environmental conservation. All books produced by The Mountaineers Books fulfill the club's mission.

Send or call for our catalog of more than 450 outdoor titles:

The Mountaineers Books
1001 SW Klickitat Way, Suite 201
Seattle, WA 98134
800-553-4453
mbooks@mountaineers.org
www.mountaineersbooks.org

Other titles you may enjoy from The Mountaineers Books:

BEARS: Monarchs of Northern Wilderness, *Wayne Lynch*
This large-format, full-color book explores bears' life cycles, communication, habits, relationships, and daily life. The brown bear, polar bear, Asiatic black bear, and American black bear are followed through four seasons.

***BACKPACKER'S* EVERYDAY WISDOM: 1001 Expert Tips for Hikers,**
Karen Berger
Expert tips and tricks for hikers and backpackers selected from one of the most popular *BACKPACKER* magazine columns. Problem-solving techniques and brilliant improvisations show hikers how to make their way and survive in the backcountry.

***BACKPACKER'S* WILDERNESS 911: A Step-by-Step Guide for Medical Emergencies and Improvised Care in the Backcountry,** *Eric A. Weiss, M.D.*
Written by a *BACKPACKER* magazine medical editor and emergency room veteran, this guide covers the injuries and incidents most likely to happen in the backcountry. Instructions for self-care are kept simple and are easy to follow.

WILDERNESS NAVIGATION: Finding Your Way Using Map, Compass, Altimeter & GPS, *Bob Burns and Mike Burns*
Backed by more than 60 years of field research, it includes the most reliable and easy-to-learn methods of navigation yet devised.

PREGNANT BEARS AND CRAWDAD EYES: Excursions & Encounters in Animal Worlds, *Paul Schullery*
Twenty-one essays illuminate the practical life of animals and how they are affected and perceived by humans.

ANIMAL TRACKS Books and Posters, *Chris Stall*
Tracks and information on 40 to 50 animals common to each region. Available for Alaska, California, Northern California, Southern California, Great Lakes, Mid-Atlantic, New England, Pacific Northwest, Rocky Mountains, Southeast, Southwest, and Texas.